Minding
the Earth

Other books by Joseph Meeker
  The Comedy of Survival (1974, 1980)
  Spheres of Life (1975)
  Ancient Roots of the Modern World (1976)
  Modern Consciousness (1978)

Minding the Earth

Thinly Disguised Essays on Human Ecology

Joseph W. Meeker

Illustrations by Sandra Noel

The Latham Foundation
Clement and Schiller Streets
Alameda, California 94501

1988

Published by The Latham Foundation
Clement and Schiller Streets
Alameda, California 94501

Book design by Helen Neill.

Library of Congress Cataloging in Publication Data
Meeker, Joseph W. 1932-
     Minding the Earth: Thinly Disguised Essays on Human Ecology
     1. Ecology, Human   2. Nature essays
Library of Congress Catalog Card Number 87-83609
ISBN 0-931735-01-7

Printed by Island Industries, Inc., Vashon Island, Washington
Set in Old Style Goudy

For Ben and Kurt

Contents

Introduction

*"I do not portray being:
I portray passing."*
—Michel de Montaigne

Minding is a serious form of play. It includes thinking about, remembering, caring, and obeying the rules on Earth. The human mind and the Earth are more gerunds than nouns, processes more than things, and together they dance and converse in an exchange of energies. A suitable form to represent these moving relationships is the essay, literally an attempt to describe passing thoughts and scenes. These essays are more glimpses than grasps, a kind of small talk with the Earth.

Since 1980, "Minding the Earth" has been the name of a public forum concerned with human ecology and environmental ethics. First it was a weekly radio program carried on many National Public Radio stations. Then a small quarterly publication bore that title, first published by The Strong Center for Environmental Values in Berkeley, then by the Latham Foundation in Alameda, California. In all its forms, "Minding the Earth" has tried to translate complex ideas from philosophy and science into the languages of ordinary discourse. The premise is that positive changes in our relationships with the Earth must grow from the values and ideas that inform human behavior. "Minding the Earth" is a thinly disguised effort to help minds feel more at home on Earth.

Hugh Tebault, president of The Latham Foundation, rescued *Minding the Earth Quarterly* from oblivion in 1984, and provided publishing support for more than three years. The Latham Foundation's purpose is "to promote respect for all life through education," and *Minding the Earth* became one of the many ways Latham serves that end. Su Schlagel, Latham's gifted office manager, gave generously of her practical and spiritual gifts. Helen Neill has given years of loving help, wise counsel, and skilled design to every part of *Minding the Earth,* and every part of me. These good people, and many others who have helped, have my permanent gratitude and love.

Joseph Meeker
Vashon Island, January, 1988

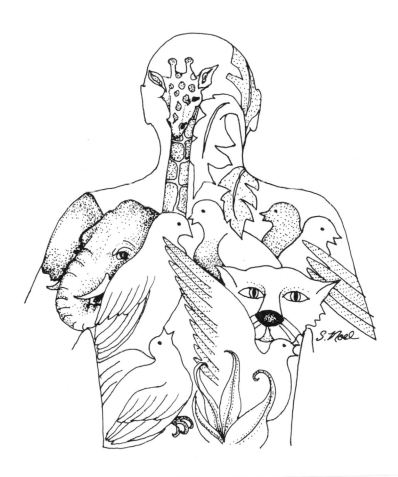

Minding One: Thinking

Thinking is the first meaning of minding. The senses reach out for news of the Earth, creating perceptions that sometimes grow into ideas. The curious mind tries to figure out how things came to be as they are, and how to find the right way to join in earthly processes. Most likely the Earth has a mind that also minds us, so thinking often feels like a reciprocal exchange between familiars.

Readings
for
Morning

A native hunter, upon arising, is likely to read the sky and the winds, feel the barometric pressure and humidity, and observe the movements of nearby animals and birds. Learning how to sort the significant from the trivial in a natural environment is a subtle process, with mastery coming only after careful learning, many mistakes, and years of practice. It is important to get it right, for the hunter's livelihood depends upon his accuracy and good judgment.

When a business investor arises, he is likely to inspect the Wall Street Journal. From it he will learn about interest rates, the money supply, market trends, and perhaps gossip and rumors about changes in management, imminent takeovers, or political winds in foreign lands. His task is also tricky, taxing all the intellectual and intuitive skills that our species has developed over the past few million years.

Most everyone, I imagine, needs a Morning Reading to help get the day off to a safe and fruitful start. Commuters scan the radio dial for news of jackknifed trucks, gardeners judge the day for decisions about transplanting, fertilizing, or pruning, and the fashion conscious may study their wardrobes in search of the perfect clothes for a smashing success. Whether it is a newspaper or a landscape, a political development or a dream sequence, the morning information session is often the key to the fate of a day.

The hunter and the investor look for very different content in their Morning Readings, but there is probably not much difference in the form of their analysis, or in the complexity of the process. It is exactly because there were generations of hunters sizing up mornings for many millenia that the human mind acquired the characteristics used today by investors. The mental abilities of our species are ancient, however modern may be the uses to which we put them.

It is too much to say that you are what you read in the morning, but it is a sure bet that you aren't what you don't. A morning that begins with numbers, words, or machines is likely to turn into a day filled with the same things. When a scanning of sky, trees, and birds begins the day, it could still turn out to be dominated by words and machines, but at least there would be a natural perspective to provide the larger context. A day that starts with a recognition of living processes can't be all bad.

It is worthwhile to pause for a moment and to reflect upon the character of the Morning Reading pursued by each of us. If a typical morning includes nothing but human acts and artifacts, then most of the Earth is being left out. Not everyone has the luxury of the hunter's wilderness landscape to ponder, but birds on a phone pole can also provide meaningful morning messages. And if nothing else, there is always the wilderness of one's own body to read, with its rivers of blood and rhythms of pulsation. A good day in the life of a living system begins with recognition and affirmation of life.

Languages
for a
Living Earth

When the storm blew over him, King Lear raged back at it: "Blow winds, and crack your cheeks." For him the Earth was alive, and the violence of its weather was matched by the anguish within himself. Most conversations with nature are less dramatic than Lear's, as we go about the daily business of expressing our aliveness by communicating with the life around us. A chat with a cat or dog is always instructive, and a word from a warbler can make the day. Plants express themselves more slowly, but like rocks, they listen very well. It is important that we pay attention to the language we use to hold up our end of the conversation with life.

Human voices are increasingly affirming that the Earth as a whole is a living organism. That is not news in the history of consciousness, for it is one of the most ancient and widespread beliefs of human thought. It has been forgotten or laid aside in recent centuries as we have pursued the premise that the Earth is inert matter or a mechanism designed to serve our needs. That period has effectively broken the ancient habit of thinking about the Earth as if it were a mother or a loved one. The new messages about a living Earth, if I understand them, do not say that the Earth is a *person*, but only that it is alive.

Lear may have been mistaken in his assumption that the wind has cheeks.

Gaia may be the wrong name for a living Earth if it conveys the impression of a personified planet. It might be more accurate to call the Earth Rover or Spot, except that it is clearly not a domesticated creature. Some people call it The Whole System, but that is too academic and smacks again of mechanism. Others address the Earth as God or Love, names that carry heavy psychological and cultural baggage. A friend, Deena Metzger, likes to call the life force Toots, a genderless name that conveys the earthy familiarity of life. That's more like it.

Names and vocabulary changes, however, are not nearly adequate to the task of finding the right language for a living Earth. Syntax must also change, and we will have to rethink the meanings of subject, predicate, object, noun, and verb. Rhythms of language need to observe the pulses of fluids and the subtleties of daily and seasonal time. Imagery can be used to conjure anew the sense and the sensations of life. And our most powerful form, metaphor, is just waiting for the inventive mind that will renew the meaning of a living Earth in the human imagination.

The best languages for a living Earth may not be verbal at all. When we stop talking and pay attention to the ways in which the Earth expresses itself, the variety is dazzling. Smells fill the air telling of ripeness, decomposition, and the subtler messages carried by pheromones. Surface textures announce the boundaries among forms. Colors invite and repel, and tastes speak of dangers and opportunities. Dance is everywhere, from mating rituals to planetary orbits. There is music throughout, in birdsong, running water, electromagnetic patterns, and in storms like the one Lear heard. Volcanoes and earthquakes express the Earth's exuberance, as poisoned water and air proclaim its illness. The languages of the Earth are eloquent beyond words.

People
and Other
Misused Resources

*Nel mezzo del cammin di nostra vita
mi ritrovai per una selva oscura
che la diritta via era smarrita.*
—Dante, *Inferno*

I n the middle of the journey of our life I came to myself in the
midst of a dark wood where I was a resource. It was one of those
retreats on a wooded island in Puget Sound, where I had been invited
as a consultant, or, as they say, a "resource person." It was not a new
role for me, but this time the participants seemed aggressively hungry
to wring from me everything I had stored within. Facts, data, personal
experience, opinions, feelings, tastes, ideas about life, art, nature, and
the stock market were lifted from me and distributed among the group
like slices of pizza. Suddenly I knew within myself what it felt like
to be a resource.

I was a forest in the process of being clearcut. I was a river being
dammed so that my energies could be diverted to others. I was a metal
deep in the Earth until someone broke through the protective layers to
extract me. The wild animal in me felt crosshairs and lenses focussed as
fingers poised on triggers and shutters. For the first time, I knew what it
meant to be a managed commodity, useful to others but with no rights
of my own. Being a resource is dangerous and degrading these days.

It was not always so. People lived for many millenia with no resources
at all. They had food, water, warmth, knowledge, and materials for

clothing and shelter, all of which came from the surrounding processes of nature, but they didn't have resources until the invention of that concept in modern times.

At its origins, the word resource was spirited and lively. Its root is the Latin *surgere,* to surge or to rise. Literally, re-source means "to rise again." A close relative is the word resurrection. An archaic form, "resourd" or "resword" was common in English through the fifteenth century, when a woman was described who did penance for her sins, "and soo reswordyd agayne to grace." By the seventeenth century the spelling had changed to its present form, but its usage still suggested renewal. The *Oxford English Dictionary* quotes a typical seventeenth century example: "For whatsoever from our hand she (the Earth) takes, Greater, or less, a vast return she makes. Nor am I only pleased with that resource." Resource, then, was the word used to describe reciprocal gifts between humans and the Earth.

The industrial era changed all that. Resources came to be associated with the wealth of nations, and as a means toward the attainment of prosperity and self-defense. By 1870, a man named Yeats (not the poet) wrote in his *Natural History Commentary:* "In speaking of the natural resources of any country we refer to the ore in the mine, the stone unquarried, the timber unfelled, etc." That was the first usage of the word resource in the sense that has come to be almost universally accepted today. Now, a little more than a century later, most dictionaries define resource as "the collective wealth of a country or its means of producing wealth," or as "any property that can be converted into money." Converting the natural world into money has become the theme of our time.

The transformation of mutual gifts into lifeless commodities by calling them resources is more than a shift of language. The Earth's gifts became resources as part of the process of depriving nature of any rights that might restrain the ways in which people use its goods. Gifts imply some reciprocity between giver and receiver, such as mutual respect and shared obligations. Gifts also imply a giver, whom the receiver must recognize and acknowledge. No such matters of conscience or courtesy exist when the Earth's goods are regarded as resources. Resources exist only as potential wealth and power for people, and forests then serve no purpose but being felled.

Something akin has often happened in the ways people use and regard their fellow humans. Psychologist Eric Erickson described a mental process he called "pseudospeciation," in which a dominant social group refers to its enemies or subjects by names of animals that may be abused with impunity. Calling the enemy a rat, dog, snake, or swine performs the expedient trick of permitting any misuse of him without guilt or responsibility. White American frontiersmen thought of Indians as wild animals, much as they regarded the buffalo. Southern slaveholders regarded their black slaves as domesticated animals, using them for hard labor and convenience as they used oxen and horses. When animal names have not been handy to identify an enemy, people have invented new species names to apply to those they want to abuse: wop, honky, gook, nigger, spic, and hosts of other pseudospecific words have allowed endless exploitation of ethnic and racial groups. The purpose of these inventions is always to deprive the enemy of rights normally accorded to other beings.

The word resource has served similar purposes. A major difference is that resources are neither enemies nor friends, but are absolutely neutral. They do not have an animal character, or any character at all. "Wildlife resources" are not animals and plants, but some vague category of matter that needs managing. We can't tell whether "energy resources" refers to petroleum, nuclear fuel, or firewood. And managers who take pride in the "human resources" of their organizations do not seem to be speaking of people, but of disembodied talents under their control. Some hidden, unspoken reality always goes unrecognized when the word resource is used. That is the point. The word resource serves the desired purpose of disguising our thoughts and actions in an abstraction that has no perceptible qualities whatsoever. Human resources, unlike people, are never rebellious. Natural resources, unlike air and water, are never polluted or exhausted. And whatever kinds of resources we refer to, we can be confident that they have no rights, no character, no life, and no values of their own. The only values attached to resources lie in the utility and wealth they provide for their managers.

What, then, is a resource? It is not the name of any creature or thing on Earth. It has no sensory qualities, and sparks no images in the mind or the imagination. It is not a metaphor that conveys a vivid relationship of any kind. It does not refer to any action, or to a state of being. It has no symbolic qualities to excite wonder, awe, love, or hatred. It is not descriptive. Just because resource lacks the evocative and communicative functions we expect from words, it has become popular in a world bent upon ignoring the implications of its actions. When we speak of resources, we can be sure that we are talking about nothing that matters.

The pervasiveness of the word resource in modern vocabularies may be a measure of how many things we prefer not to take seriously. When we are unwilling to address specific causes, lumping them under some vague problem of resources seems to relieve us of concern. Businesses fail for lack of resources. Conservation organizations plead for stewardship of resources, and exhort us to preserve the wilderness resources that constitute our national wealth. Street people live as they do because they lack resources. Without inner resources, people are subject to whims and fantasies, and they are likely to be exploited as resources for others. Government agencies created to protect natural resources are themselves resources in the service of destructive land use industries. All around us are cultural resources, intellectual resources, spiritual resources, personal resources, financial resources, food resources, entertainment resources. We are all resource people living in a fuzzy world of resources. Every novel use of the term subtracts something concrete from our perceptions and adds a measure of abstraction, and irresponsibility, to our lives.

Yet while we abuse the word resources and the things and processes it has come to stand for, another kind of resurgence is also growing among us. There is emerging a renewed awareness of the ancient idea that the Earth is a living organism, and is not merely an aggregation of useful, inert, matter. The idea is not the plaything of soft-minded environmentalists, but a carefully reasoned hypothesis growing among thinkers with impeccable philosophic and scientific credentials. British geochemist James Lovelock, with biologist Lynn Margulis, formulated the hypothesis and named it for the Greek goddess of the Earth, *Gaia*. The Gaia Hypothesis grew from studies of atmospheric self-regulatory systems, and has developed through meticulous studies into a perception of the self-organizing character of planetary systems. Its roots are in the scientific theories and techniques of systemic analysis, not in the ethics of conservation.

James Lovelock, in *Gaia: A New Look at Life on Earth* (London, Oxford University Press, 1982), provides a simple and clear statement of the Gaia Hypothesis:

> "The entire range of living matter on Earth, from whales to viruses, and from oaks to algae, could be regarded as a single living entity, capable of manipulating the Earth's atmosphere to suit its overall needs and endowed with faculties and powers far beyond those of its constituent parts."

Many living systems whose powers are greater than the sums of their parts have been studied as interactive systems. The human body is one such system, as are most other animals and plants. Communities of organisms often operate according to self-regulating systemic principles. The science of ecology, at its best, studies self-organizing natural structures of immense complexity. The emergence of systemic thinking over the past half-century has created both the cultural climate and the intellectual perspectives necessary for imagining whole systems in which the relationships among constituent parts are more vital than any part alone. It seems natural that this new perception should now be applied to the Earth.

Perhaps it is unfortunate that Lovelock's hypothesis has been given a personal name, Gaia. To say that the Earth is alive is not equivalent to saying that it is human-like, as the goddess' name may suggest. The name invokes images of Mother Earth, together with all of the psychological and cultural implications that such an image carries. Inspirational as such messages may sometimes be, they also are inseparable from our personal and social experiences with mothers, most of which are not systemic at all. Mothers, even more than other people, are often treated as resources are. Childhood teaches us that mothers supply needs, but not that they are parts of a much larger system of reciprocal life support.

The living Earth is not our mother, not our resource, and not ours. Our habit of naming things creates in us the illusion that we have power and control over whatever we give names to, and provides us with the security of feeling that we are on a first-name basis with our surroundings. Ancestors who thought of the Earth as a turtle's back or as a bear were closer to the mark than we are when we regard the Earth as a mother, or as a mine, or as our possession. At least the names they chose represented wild creatures whose lives are not governed by human preferences. Whatever the Earth is, it is surely a wild creature with a life of its own.

Wild is simply the name for things and processes that are not under human control. The atmosphere is wild, even when its weather is calm. Geologic processes are wild systems. The oceans are wilderness. All but a tiny handful, a fraction of one percent, of all plants and animals are wild creatures. And we began our career upon Earth as wild animals, with those roots deep in our bodies and psyches still guiding most of our behavior. We are fundamentally a part of the wild, living context of the Earth, and the small taming and domesticating we have performed upon the surfaces of our selves and the surfaces of the land have not changed the self-governing character of either. The Earth remains free, and we are freer than we let ourselves think.

We are free, for instance, to redefine the words and images we use to describe our relationships with the Earth and its processes. Our thoughts and feelings govern the words we use, so we must begin by reconsidering the meanings of this living context we are involved with. Creating new vocabularies is unnecessary, for we have long known and named our best perceptions. We only need to remember.

Earth is a good name for the Earth, for it conveys at once the sense of the dirt beneath our feet and of the planet as a whole. The Earth feels alive to us, yet it is not a person to be supplicated, manipulated, seduced, or managed. It has its own character which is not to be confused with human character, for it is the context that includes all creatures. It does not exist for human benefit, but it both benefits and disciplines all life forms. And it is not alone, but is one of many spheres in a cosmos that is also alive. Its relationships to stars and other planets are more significant for the Earth's life than are any of the creatures living on its surface. The Earth has its own life to live, and we are willy-nilly a temporary part of that living.

Our perspective is usually smaller, as we grub for our needs in the dirt that is a thin layer of the Earth. Here we have lately discovered resources, replacing what we had earlier thought of as goods and gifts. We were right the first time, for the useful products of earthly processes are *goods:* they have worth and value, and they are to be prized and respected. They are also *gifts:* unearned benefits that grow from a reciprocal relationship between ourselves and the Earth. And they entail us in an obligation to give something beneficial in return. Goods and gifts are accurate and meaningful words for the things we use to support ourselves from the Earth. They are appropriate to the emerging human role as responsible participants in the activities of the living Earth.

Awakening to find that I was a resource ruined my day, but it led to better days ahead. It was one of those rare epiphanies, as when a book or a film or a conversation creates genuine empathy to reveal what it feels like to be a black slave on a plantation, or a woman in the hands of a rapist, or a wild animal on display in a zoo. I will never willingly be a resource person again, although I am happy to be in the role of friend, helper, mentor, or teacher. Someday it would be grand to be a gift person, or with luck even a good person. But henceforth, I am without resources.

I want the Earth to be free of resources as well, and I personally declare it to be so. Since my experience as a resource person three years ago, I have tried to rinse away resources from my mind and my language. It has been a wonderful experience. Whenever I see the word in print, I mentally edit the text to substitute the real things that are being referred to, if any. Mideast resources become oil; capital resources become money; agricultural resources become soil or farmers or machinery, depending upon the context; wildlife resources are animals needed for hunting, scientific study, or tourism; scenic resources are spectacular landscapes; forest resources are marketable timber; educational resources are teachers, libraries, or classrooms; human resources are employees; inner resources are strength of character. As resource has disappeared from my vocabulary, my thinking has become more tangible and concrete.

When it is necessary to refer to larger categories of things, alternatives to resources usually improve clarity and change meaning in healthy ways. I like to think of governments establishing departments of natural goods to replace agencies of natural resources. It would be fine if children could be taught about conservation of natural gifts. Emerging nations should be encouraged to develop their natural gifts rather than to exploit their resources. Even "source" is a big improvement over "resource," for a source is at least the recognized origin of something; a water source is a particular stream or well, but water resources are without place or identity. Whenever the word resource is replaced, things seem to become more interesting, more real.

The rediscovery that the Earth is alive means that we can and should enter into conversation with it. That requires recognition of its particular characteristics and suitable language to describe them. The words we choose need also to reflect the responsibilities and mutual exchanges we honor in our relationship with the Earth. Resource was a word coined to deprive the Earth and its goods of meaning, and to permit irresponsibility in their use. Apologies for that misuse are now in order, together with some gift-giving of our own to make amends for our disrespect. What does one give to an Earth that seems to have everything? A friendly greeting would be a good way to begin, followed by a little gratitude, and a resolution to use careful language in our continuing conversation.

Nurturing
Chaos

E cology is getting organized, but not very ecologically. A blizzard
of eco-organizations storms through public life, sometimes
obscuring clear sight or burying important landmarks. Organizations
confer only limited kinds of order upon their chosen pieces of
reality. Each carves a hole for itself and moves in, thus limiting its
peripheral vision.

The many interests of ecological organizations take only a few
familiar forms. Eco-technology has simply become good business.
Green politicians have won power in Europe, and will soon do so
in North America. Every university has a department of environmental studies, plus its scientific ecologists who now build elaborate
computer models and study ecosystems via satellite. If you aspire to
be an ecoteur, you can buy manuals of ecotage. If you prefer to
withdraw, there is ecomonasticism. The Eleventh Commandment has
been proclaimed: "Thou shalt not despoil the earth nor destroy the
life thereon." Wilderness retreats offer mental and physical health,
or ecological hospice care for those who are beyond health.

There is surely much more going on, but that list gives the flavor
of the varieties of ecological experience available. Few of these

activities could survive without good organizations to support them. To make such an organization requires that a problem or an opportunity be identified, and that a dedicated group of people be found who take that problem or opportunity very seriously. Then it is only necessary to choose the form of the organization from among the following possibilities:

1. *Business.* Found a (non-profit?) corporation, enlist big names for the letterhead, publish a newsletter, plan media projects, raise funds, build a constituency, create events of high visibility.

2. *Academic.* Identify a special area of inquiry, define it so as to exclude all others, prove that all prior studies have missed the point, found a department, then proceed as businesses do (see above).

3. *Religious.* Identify the enemy, preach a simple and clear message of good and evil, practice virtues and oppose vices, promise distant rewards, and proceed as businesses do (see above).

Although ecological organizations may have a new message, they usually adhere to these basic forms and techniques traditionally used by the organizations they hope to oppose or replace. The forms were created by a pre-ecological time in order to exercise power over people and events. Aggression is normally mobilized within them, and is fostered by them. People within such organizations, just like Yuppies in electronics, can be expected to burn out young because they are always living with crisis. And the organizations themselves, even when they succeed with a new agenda, continue to perpetuate by example the worn and inappropriate methods of the past.

It makes sense that ecological purposes should be pursued by ecological forms and methods. The change of consciousness that goes by the name of ecology should soon be ready to move beyond its pioneering stage. The tough, singleminded forms resembling fireweed and willows are still visible in the tenacious groups organized around their passionate purposes. They have their own special beauty and vitality, but they will not be suitable much longer. More complex and more elegant forms will emerge, and their shape and character will fit new niches. Surely they will learn how to laugh sometime soon, and eventually birds may sing and breed in their upper reaches. When environmentalism begins to resemble in form the wild systems it wishes to protect, then succession will be the clearest sign of success.

In the 4th century B.C., the ironies involved in organizing to serve good purposes were recognized by the Taoist Chuang-Tzu. He tells how Fuss, a southern god, and Fret, a northern god, chanced to meet in the realm of Chaos, the god of the center. Chaos treated them well and they wanted to repay his kindness. They had noticed that Chaos had no apertures in his body such as others had for eating, breathing, excreting and so on. For his benefit, they organized themselves to bore a hole in Chaos every day. When they bored the last hole, Chaos died.

The god of the center is still Chaos. Some prefer to call him Wilderness, others call him The Whole System, and others call her Mother. Chaos is all genders, all forms, all time, all possibilities. If the apertures of Chaos are not arranged in familiar ways, or if there are none visible, it is not the task of Fret and Fuss to fix things. A better job for them would be to learn how to live at peace with Chaos, for from Chaos comes the only genuine order we know.

Well-Tempered Ecology

S pring is the time when the Earth tunes up for its annual
polyphonic performance. Birds that were silent much of
the winter suddenly remember their cadenzas and practice them
endlessly, while their squeaky-voiced offspring learn by imitation the
musical score that is particular to their species. Choruses of frogs
celebrate the life of ponds. Migrant whales and birds sing navigational
advice and encouragement to one another. Wolves howl during long
arctic evenings. Breezes pass back and forth across new leaves like
bows over fiddles. The cycle of the seasons is a musical composition,
and the Earth is its instrument.

Human music tries to fit into the Earth's chorus, but with uneven
success. As long as our kind has been on Earth, we have made music
with vibrating strings and vocal chords, pounded rhythms on skins
and logs, and fingered holes in air columns to tune our flutes and
kazoos. Our musical sounds resembled those made by other animals
until fairly recently, when our technology took a turn that modified
the music of this sphere.

The sweeping changes of the seventeenth century industrial
revolution brought us steam engines, keyboard instruments, and
Johann Sebastian Bach. Medieval and Renaissance modes of music

disappeared in favor of a new system of tonal organization called tempering which made tones available in a variety of different keys. The time was ripe for Bach to demonstrate the abundant possibilities of a new technology and a new musical vision in the forty-eight compositions known as *The Well-Tempered Clavier*.

Another tool more recently invented is called ecology. Ecology is a mental device, a metaphor, invented in the late nineteenth century when it became necessary to notice that the Earth is the home and habitat of all living creatures. The Earth had always been that way, but western culture could not begin to see the intricate webs of life until it fashioned ecological spectacles. Science had become our main way of seeing, so we first thought of ecology as a part of biological science. It is still that, and scientific ecology is growing rapidly in the sophistication of its techniques and the comprehensiveness of its theories.

Yet ecology is not only a science, for it also retains vigor as a metaphor that suggests that *Oikos*, house, is a total set of living contexts and relationships that must be attended to. Metaphors always tickle the mind toward novel interpretations. Plenty have popped up around ecology, from the early stages of conservation thinking, land ethics, and environmentalism to more recent ideas of stewardship, environmental law and politics, eco-activism and ecotage, and philosophies of deep ecology. Ecological themes and variations abound, but harmony among them is rare.

No ecological Bach is like to appear to organize and synthesize the diverse strains of ecology, and no such person is appropriate now. We seem to have passed beyond the time when a single genius could give expression to the meaning of an era. Whatever meanings we find are more likely to arise from a shared consciousness to which many minds and souls have contributed. But together perhaps we can learn a little from Bach about how to make harmony and beauty out of a grand jumble. It may be a matter of temperament.

Latin *temperare* is a rich root, meaning "to combine in due proportion." Earlier antecedents suggest that the word arose from the need to express perceptions of continuity in space and time. During a few thousand years of usage in several languages, *temperare* has developed an impressive progeny of related words. Our temporal sense tells us where we are in time, and when we temper metals with heat or carbon we alter their spatial density and harden them. We can also lose our tempers and become ill-tempered. Non-durable things are temporary, and pleasant climates are temperate because they have comfortable temperatures and few tempests. Unnecessary meddling is tampering, which can lead to distemper or worse. Intemperate people are sometimes tempestuous or temperamental, and they tend to be mindless of their contemporaries. Imaginative folks can extemporize on their feet, or they may temporize if they choose to stall. A temple may be either a place of worship or the space above our eyes, and both are suited for contemplation.

Well-tempered ecology can draw upon much of this temperamental imagery. Surely ecology must be a science and a philosophy deeply concerned with due proportions. This is its systemic aspect, investigating relationships in time and space and explaining the mysteries of evolution, ecological succession, and the behavioral implications of natural forms and processes. But ecology can also be tempered as steel is: hardened and made capable of sustaining a sharp edge. The tough temper of ecology could provide an antidote to the forms of cute and sentimental ecology that parade in public under the banner of the Disney Syndrome. Well-tempered ecology will need, too, to create a musical tempo of dance and song so that it can realize its inherent artistry and discover the proportions of beauty.

Well-tempered ecology necessarily includes a strong contemplative aspect, yet it also needs to be temporal in both senses: intimately connected with daily life and action, and acutely aware of the scope of cosmic and earthly time. It can resolve the unreal separation between action and contemplation by recognizing that each is an essential part of the other. Reflection and wisdom are included in the natural history of the Earth, just as work and conflict are.

I can hear a five-part fugue of well-tempered ecology, developing the themes of proportionality, tempered hardness, lively tempo, contemplation, and temporality. The complex fingering will be performed by the human mind, and the rhythms will be those of the Earth. I can't tell whether it sounds more like Bach, Bartok, or the Beatles, but it rings as true as the genuineness that is in all of them. Mostly, it sounds like significant play. Music and ecology must both be played with love and skill if they are to be heard, felt, and understood.

On
Edges

Living on an island makes me aware that everybody does. John Donne's observation that "no man is an island" is convertible to its opposite, everyone is an island, depending upon whether one prefers to emphasize autonomy or interconnectedness. Both are facts of life, all life. The sea that forms a moat about my home is a spatial edge, and it resembles the temporal edge of nightime that distinguishes yesterday from today. Recognition of boundaries is serious business for all creatures of the Earth, as is crossing them.

It was on an island in the Galapagos Archipelago where Darwin met birds that set him thinking. Musing upon variations in mocking-birds, young Darwin wrote in his diary that these islands would be "well worth examination, for such facts would undermine the stability of species." The evolutionary ideas that Darwin explored on those islands have reverberated through modern consciousness. Exploration around the edge of things often undermines stability, but it also encourages the growth of new forms and new perceptions.

Ecotone is the name for the place where ecological systems meet. It is an area devoted to gradation, like a beach that includes several distinguishable zones between the lowest and highest tides, with different living creatures occupying each zone. Walking the beach is an experience of marine life on one hand and terrestrial life on the other. Between them the beachcomber learns about what the two have to say to one another, for underfoot are the gifts and tributes they mutually offer. Ecotones separate natural systems, and bind them together through the permeable boundaries they share.

Boundaries in time are often known as epochs. Long periods of accumulating snow added up to Pleistocene glaciation, the climatic consequences of which are still with us. Gradual accumulations of people and ideas made possible a classical Greece, which ended as a civilization but continues today as a powerful influence. Other ancient civilizations ended abruptly with little left to show that they ever existed, crushed by warfare or covered by the silts of erosion from their denuded watersheds. Most change moves more slowly. Marine creatures learned a bit at a time how to breathe air and eventually crossed the beaches to become land animals. Some land animals fanned themselves for millenia with appendages that were later to evolve into wings, permitting them to cross the boundary between Earth and sky. It generally takes time to create a new form, or to extinguish one, for time, like natural space, is a matter of gradation from one stage to another.

Natural edges are seldom abrupt. Boundary areas tend to be littered with debris that tells the story of passages across them. Succession in a forest ecosystem leaves the forest floor fertilized by species of plants and animals whose stages of life have come and gone. Ideas that were new a century or two ago often clutter minds that need to cope with today. The past persists, both as impediment and as guide. Even inveterate boundary-crossers like migrating birds and fish have found ways to leave genetic memory paths so that succeeding generations can find their ways around the Earth without help. Passage from place to place or from time to time tends to leave trails.

Much of human technology and social history looks like a massive effort to shore up boundaries and to make them as sharp and impermeable as possible. Ancient clay vessels held water poorly until someone invented firing and glazing to harden their walls. Metals were mined to increase the durability of edges like wheel rims, and because they could be sharpened to a fine edge. Stones proved useful for building walls around homes and cities, or a Great Wall in China, or even a wall against death like the pyramids. The human desire for impermeability has given us an age of plastics and a quest for tamper-proof packaging. Ancient pots still hold water today, but few other human barriers have accomplished their purposes. Seawalls seldom shut out the sea for long, castles notoriously fail to defend their builders, and packages are tampered with. "Something there is," said Robert Frost, "that doesn't love a wall." The Something includes both nature and humanity.

Walls of words and symbols may work better than those of stone. We and They are boundary words that have cost many millions of human lives to maintain, and we continue to strengthen them. Laws and treaties create borders on the Earth in defiance of natural patterns, yet we defend them with as much passion as a bird shows for its nesting territory. Descartes drew a philosophical line between mind and body that has skewed our thinking for three centuries. Symbols of spirit and culture separate Moslems and Jews, Catholics and Protestants. Boundaries based only upon beliefs have a way of creating enemies.

When art is involved, edges resemble ecotones more than barriers. Well told stories neither begin nor end in definitive ways: "once upon a time" is both now and then. James Joyce's *Finnegan's Wake* ends with a partial sentence that is completed on the first page of the book, illustrating the cyclic time through which literature normally moves. The best paintings refuse to remain within their frames, and good sculpture soars from its pedestal. Music is audible liquid time, with rhythms and resonances that penetrate our bodies. Musical beginnings and endings are arbitrary affairs, as if the composer were merely snipping out a piece of an ongoing process to present in public, while the real music just goes on and on. Like prairie moving toward mountains, the edges of art are indistinct.

Skin seems like a separator until you notice how much there is that passes through it as it breathes, sweats, absorbs, and responds to sensations. With fur added, skin becomes an even fuzzier boundary between inside and outside; you don't have to touch a cat to elicit a twitch. Taoists long ago noticed that the usefulness of house walls depends upon the emptiness of doors and windows, and that vessels have utility only because they can be poured into and out of. Youth, maturity, and age are graded stages that overlap for all living creatures. Even birth and death seem more like bridges than boundaries.

The ferry that links my island to the mainland deserves more respect than I usually give it. Crossing over boundaries is one of the best things my species has learned how to do. Friendship is one ferry that spans the seas between us, and love is another. Spirit is boundless, and it ties us to the plants, the animals, to one another, and to the Earth itself. Our highest esteem is reserved for those processes that create passages over boundaries. Like customs, boundaries are more honored in the breach than the observance.

Yet islands really are islands, and all creatures live on one, or on many. We are male or female, mammal or crustacean, deciduous or evergreen, youthful or aging. At some far less significant level I suppose we are also Russians or Americans, rich or poor, fashionable or faded. Some distinctions matter less than others. Our most genuine boundaries deserve our best attention, for within them lie our security and identity. They are our own places. Their edges provide stimulation, change, and novelty. The great thing about boundaries is that they all have openings that can be left ajar. The ferries do cross over, even when they are not running on time.

Who Needs
Wild Creatures?

S ince all life lives from other life, all of us animals need one another. But the obvious importance of evolutionary history and daily nourishment are not nearly enough to explain the fundamental bond that ties us to the animals with whom we share the planet. Our connections with animals span the depths of time, space, mind, and spirit. Without them, we cannot truly become ourselves.

Living with a pet seems a simple enough thing on the surface, but when you look fully at the implications of household pets, the complexities are vast. It is perhaps fortunate that some parents don't know what they are getting into when they buy a puppy or kitten for their toddler, or they might never take that first step (in some cases they shouldn't). One motive parents have for adding an animal to their household is to help their children "learn responsibility." Feeding and caring for an animal are supposed to teach the child to keep a regular schedule for meals and cleanup. Moms everywhere know that it often doesn't work that way, for they end up doing the daily chores while the child concentrates on what it most needs and wants from the pet: fuzzy love uncluttered by rules.

Children rarely need to be taught to love an animal, for that comes naturally. Why should it? The answer lies in several millions of years of close sharing that have passed between humans and other creatures. Whether wild or domesticated, animals have played a major role in shaping the emotional and mental lives of people as long as they have been around on the planet. Every culture is rich in animal stories for children, and these have grown from direct experiences and deep wisdom accumulated over trackless time. The animals in the best children's tales are not mere symbols for abstract ideas or moral rules; they are the bearers of truths which cannot be learned in any other way. When an American Indian child learns of the many ways of the coyote, he or she is learning how the world works.

A kitten or a coyote can teach any child much about the realities of the world. Love is one of those lessons, but only one among many. A growing child often has its first experience of illness, injury, or death through an animal it has known. Caring for a sick cat or grieving at the irreversibility of its death often shapes how a child will react to those experiences in mature life. How to handle feelings of aggression and fear are other lessons we often learn from animals. Birds teach music, and our minds learn to soar in imagination on their wings. Several dozen garden spiders in my childhood taught me the beauty and practicality of webs, and the structural principles that underlie good form and good engineering.

Human relationships with animals are usually reciprocal; when we perceive them, we are also being perceived by them. One wonders what animals may learn from us? Perhaps not much, for astonishingly few of them have chosen to sit at our feet. Of the millions of animal species on the planet, only a handful—less than fifty—have proved susceptible to domestication. The vast majority cannot (will not?) adapt their ways of living to the lifestyles of humans, and those that have done so often find good cause to regret it.

The process of domistication requires that we find ways to weaken or to compromise the basic integrity of an animal species, and to prevent it from attaining normal maturity. We feed it, so it loses its ability to earn its own living. We restrain its movement, so it becomes lethargic and sedentary. We regulate its normal social relations and sexual life, so it becomes neurotic or bizarre compared to its wild relatives. And our attempts at breeding and genetic engineering often distort its physical characteristics drastically. If domestic animals sometimes seem beastly, it is because humans have made them so.

Instead of teaching by example, as animals do for us, we prefer to train them to perform for our gain or pleasure. The applause when a dolphin or lion leaps through a hoop of flame has been earned by the trainer, and does not reflect our understanding of the marvels that those animals are, in and of themselves. Such displays perpetuate the myth that humans are in control of the natural world, and actually work against our need for better understanding of animal life. Zoos display caged and begging creatures, usually behaving abnormally. Yet even from these warped and wounded animals we can learn about ourselves and the world.

Some borderline animals live on the fringes of human influence, accepting and rejecting our ways as they see fit. Cats are like that. Whether we have domesticated cats, or they us, is a question cat owners and biologists can debate for hours. It was that way with the quarter-wolf malamute sled dogs I used to work with in Alaska. Their domestication was only skin deep, and they never let me indulge in the illusion that I was in control of their lives. If they did what I wished, it was clearly because they had decided to do so, and it told me that they had accepted me as a cooperating member of their group. Often that didn't work, and I did things their way. Efficiency is not among the chartacteristics of dog sledding.

One of the strongest dogs, Joe, was a marvel of energy and a terror to try to manage. He was the team comedian, loving to play tricks, clown around, or pull surprises out of nowhere. Sometimes he was a bully, snarling at weaker dogs or at me over a scrap of food when I knew he was fully fed and just wanted to display his power. I was ready for danger or buffoonery whenever I approached him, and he provided both. But when Joe was seriously injured in a fight with several dogs, and was gashed to the bone from his nose to the back of his head, he let me hold his head in my lap while he was sewed up with needle and thread and no anaesthetic. In his eyes I saw trust, affection, and gratitude, mingled with his fear and pain. In a couple of weeks, he was his normal crazy self again, but the bond between us was stronger. I count Joe among the better teachers I have known in my life.

As a graduate student in wildlife ecology, I was told that wild animals are a "crop" to be managed like any other crop for maximum human benefit. I debated that as best I could using the puny powers available to students, but soon realized that I was up against an argument that was deeply imbedded in the culture and enforced by its institutions. Feeling the wrongness of that belief, but unable to get around it, I leaped when I was offered a job as ranger at Mt. McKinley (now Denali) National Park in Alaska. That began the most significant educational experience of my life, living for two years in the midst of one of the continent's last remaining wildlife concentrations, studying the animals, sharing a wilderness with them, and learning, as they must, how to cope with a very harsh environment.

Of the many animals I became close to, both scientifically and emotionally, the Alaskan moose (*Alces gigas*) strangely stood out as a creature of great importance to me. Something about its movement, color, shape, demeanor, and character spoke more deeply to me than other animals. It looked, and was, an ancient creature whose form had not changed for many millenia, and it carried its inherited antiquity with grace and dignity. I learned all I could about moose, studying in books and laboratories, and spending many hours watching, photographing, and drinking in mooseness with everything I had. Now and then I overstepped the boundaries, and was sent scurrying up a tree by bulls defending their space or by cows fearful that I might harm their calves. Even these encounters increased my awareness that the moose was a creature of spiritual importance to me: I had discovered my totem animal.

Totem animals (or plants, or mountains) have been an essential means of self-discovery for most of the people who have lived on Earth.

A totem is something separate from oneself, living by its own rules, not under human control, yet still expressive of one's personal spirit and meaning in life. It is at once an image of the Otherness of natural creation, and of the close connectedness that humans share with the natural world. Anyone who lacks a totem, I think, is living in a state of spiritual, emotional, and intellectual deprivation.

Clever people that we are, we create substitutes for totems because they are hard to find in urban or industrialized places. Teenagers who in saner times would have been embarking on vision quests in search of their totems, instead yearn for automobiles named for powerful animals: lynx, falcon, bobcat, cougar, or the sacred thunderbird. Their sports teams have names like tigers, lions, bears, eagles, or other fearsome wild creatures. A young person can get a semblance of identity from association with machines or groups of people named for wild animals, but that is a far cry from the real thing of knowing personally the genuine animal that links a person with the planet.

Humans are a unique species of animal, but then so are all the others. The interplay among species is a game of Usness and Otherness for all creatures who play it. From our point of view, animals are the Others, different from us in many ways but resembling us enough so that we can recognize important parts of ourselves in their forms, behavior, and relationships. It is difficult to guess what we might mean to another species, but there is no doubt that we have affected their lives in countless ways. Many animals might describe us as the Others who often disregard the rules of life. But the responsibility of all species is the same: to fulfill the potential that exists in every life form as fully as possible. I must try to become as complete a man as I can, just as a moose must try to become a complete moose.

The fulfillment of any given life cannot occur in isolation. Maturity grows from interactions at every stage of life. Although we may pretend that interactions with other people are the only essential contacts that will help us to grow, deep within us we know better. Reaching out to other animals is a normal and necessary part of every human life, and it is a rare or deformed person who does not do so in one way or another. There is a voice within us to say that we cannot completely be Us unless we somehow make contact with all that Otherness.

Pets are the nearest animals to most American families. Even though many generations of domestication separate them from their wild ancestors, still they are parts of the Other. It is a mistake to think of a pet as a piece of owned property whose life is fully controlled by a human master. Love and mutual respect are the most important things to strive for in relationships with a household animal, and the idea of ownership impedes those feelings. Pets should be observed closely and listened to for what they have to teach us. Their approach to problems that must be solved, pains that must be relieved, and relationships that must be nurtured are different from ours, but instructive to us none the less. To regard a dog or cat as your teacher is an important first step toward discovering humility before life, and the rewards of taking more steps in that direction are very great.

Pets may be the most obvious animals in and around our homes, but they are not as abundant, nor as instructive, as the wild animals that live with us. Every home has its spiders, who have been known for many millenia as great teachers to humans. An hour spent now and then watching a spider build and maintain her web is well invested if it can teach the wonderful combination of calm patience, swift and purposeful action, and careful creativeness that spiders know so well. Near my desk I keep a diagram of the stages in the construction of a typical spider web to remind me of the step-at-a-time attentiveness that is necessary to create anything that will be both beautiful and practical. I also share my office with quite a few real spiders who daily add footnotes and appendices to the lifeless diagram on the wall. Other small creatures drop in from time to time bearing different lessons, like the wasps who fly in the window to hunt spiders, or the squirrel who chatters news to me while digging for acorns in my potted plants.

Companionable participation, not power, is the best gift we can offer to life. Differences between human and non-human forms of life are abundant and wonderfully instructive. Every plant and animal demonstrates a different way of life, reminding us of the richness and diversity of styles that are possible in the processes of being. What we share with them, however, is at least as profound as our differences from them. Together, we are all participants in the planet's experiment in living. If we can understand what that means, then human self-interest and the preservation of other creatures become one cause and one connected experience.

Self-interest is inevitable, and is a normal part of the game of life. If elephants or salamanders felt that they were the most important and potent creatures on Earth, and forgot that they were members of the living community, it is a safe bet that they would legislate in their own best interests much as people do. Perhaps the dinosaurs ruled the Earth for their own benefit, and look how they turned out: extinct. We needn't follow their example.

Creative
Worrying

My home is within a few miles of some excellent nuclear targets: an Air Force base, a major military manufacturer, and a nuclear submarine base. There are also large trees near my house which could crush it if they fell. Shall I worry more about warfare, or about windfalls? I know what to do to protect the house from the trees, but still I can't bring myself to cut them down. I'm much less sure what to do about warfare, yet I worry about it. Both problems deserve and get my worry time, but they must share it with my concerns for extinctions of species, deforestation, climate change, overpopulation, toxic wastes, AIDS, the IRS, and those deadlines I've promised to meet next week. I am wealthy with worries.

A wise friend, David Sokoloff, offers two obvious truths about worrying:

You can't worry about everything
You can't worry all the time.

You can't because if you did you would surely achieve a paralysis preventing any action, creative thought, or fun out of life. News media bring us boatloads of worrisome information every day, and the effect upon many is numbness or neurosis. The media need not be blamed (though we can worry about their influence, too), because it is manifestly true, without media confirmation, that we live in a risky and dangerous time on a fragile and threatened planet.

Worry is a form of anxiety and anxiety is a special kind of attentiveness to the world which humans share with many other creatures. The difference is that human worries are more particular and that they are a product of consciousness, while anxiety is a state of mental and bodily fear for which there may or may not be a name. Psychoanalyst Anthony Storr says that, biologically, "anxiety is really preparation for action: for fight, or for flight from situations which you either need to get out of or need to master." A deer surprised by a hiker in the forest is anxious, and must somehow decide whether fight, flight, or indifference is its most appropriate response to the stranger that has appeared from nowhere. Many deer die because they choose wrongly, just as humans often do.

At its best, worrying is being wary and watchful, and it can and should lead toward safe and appropriate actions. But our occasions for worry have taken a quantum leap of late; they are so large that we lack the means to respond to them, and they are governed by forces far removed from our influence. A deer may run to safety from a hunter, but where can we run from a multiple warhead or a poisoned water supply? And can we trust the judgment of politicians and other powerful people whose fingers are on the various buttons that can convert our worries into realities? Probably not.

To worry is to care, not only in the sense of having cares and woes, but in the more constructive sense of being careful and taking care. Motherly care for a child springs from the same roots as demonstrating against nuclear development or condominium sprawls. Personal worries we can handle ourselves, but bigger ones require that caring people come together to act in support of life on Earth. Because of the abundance of available worries, it is necessary to choose those to act upon where we can hope to have a positive influence. Every person is responsible for deciding how to express their care for life.

If we can't worry about everything all the time, neither can we abdicate our obligation for creative worrying. The worry-free smart guys who have a pat answer for every problem, and the numb blank-eyed boobs who have passed caring, are not models we dare to follow. The trick is to worry with a focus, and to make worrying count. Careful worrying, like love, grows in strength and breadth as it is exercised, and it does make good things happen.

Oration
on the
Dignity of All

In December, 1486, an energetic young intellectual named Giovanni Pico della Mirandola (Pico to his friends) distributed in Rome a long list of nine hundred debate topics, with an invitation to scholars to join him in a public disputation about them in January, 1487. The debate never happened because some of his ideas had a whiff of heresy to them, but Pico's introductory oration for the debate somehow survived and was published after the young man's early death in 1494. Five hundred years ago, Pico's *Oration on the Dignity of Man* was laid as one of the cornerstones of modern humanism.

That unpublished keynote speech written for a conference that was never held has turned out to be one of the most powerful influences upon the modern mind. Its basic messages, that humans are free to choose whatever role they wish to play in life, and that human dignity rests upon the ability to rise mentally above nature, have been repeated so often and in so many forms that they have come to seem like gospel. But they began as heresy from a precocious New Age guru of the early Renaissance. And they are still subject to debate.

One recent manifestation of Pico's debate is in the quarrel between Christian fundamentalists and "secular humanists" over the content of textbooks in public schools. Five centuries have not been enough to change many of the issues Pico argued about: the humanists still insist on the freedom of the human mind to choose among all of the world's possibilities, and their opponents continue to insist that some heresies should not appear in public. Eavesdropping on their discussions, it is hard to avoid the feeling that both sides are, at least, slightly archaic. Pico and the Pope did it better.

More modern is the fracas between humanists and sociobiologists. Again human freedom and dignity are at stake, for sociobiologists argue that much important human behavior is guided by genetic inheritance, and that humans are more deeply rooted in nature than they are transcendant over it. Just as early humanists declined to be pushed around by popes, their modern counterparts deny that DNA can dictate what they do. Humanists refuse to give up unrestricted freedom of choice and human uniqueness, and they continue to insist, as Pico did, that the Earth is humanity's oyster.

Sometimes I wonder what this five hundred year old debate is really about. Are the opponents haggling over what they believe to be true, or over what they prefer to think about the role of humanity on Earth? Is it a question of taste? A matter of self-image? Or are different persistent parts of old cultural traditions still at war with one another long after their battlefields have gone to weed?

It is hard to believe that the dignity of humanity depends upon the affirmation of absolute freedom of choice. Pico rejoiced over the "most marvelous felicity of man. To him it is granted to have whatever he chooses, to be whatever he wills." Well, yes, but looking back over the past few centuries of people grabbing what they choose and working their will upon the world is like revisiting a woodland of one's childhood that has been paved for a shopping mall. Pico's pride converted easily into merciless exploitation of both the planet and its less powerful people, millions of whom still see precious little evidence of their freedom and dignity. And the Earth itself groans under the burden of such a glorified humanity.

Perhaps it is time we had an oration on the dignity of moose. Moose, too, are free to choose among almost endless options; they can have whatever they choose and be whatever they will, provided only that they remain consistent with moose character, biology, and habitat. They tower proudly over the lesser species around them, and they defend themselves effectively against all attacks except the final one of death. Cow moose are careful parents, spending full time in loving companionship with their offspring and encouraging them toward maturity and independence when the time is ripe. Bulls are more contemplative most of the time. They spend countless hours in meditation, perhaps in preparation for the contests of mating season where they display their wit and prowess. Moose seem to strive with every action of their lives to fulfill the highest standards of moosehood. What more can be asked of any species?

When we have dignified the moose, we can proceed through the taxonomic tables to do the same for all other species. Dignity will come easily for llamas and members of the cat family, but it may be harder to grasp for mosquitos, slugs, crabgrass, and the AIDS virus. The qualifications for dignity, however, will remain the same for all species that live free lives, and they are close to the standards that Pico applied: freedom must be used to realize the full possibilities of one's own nature in a manner that is appropriate to one's time, place, and circumstance. Pico merely made explicit those principles that guide the lives of all wild creatures.

Only those species lacking freedom of choice need to philosophize and to develop strategies to attain it so that they may have a chance to become what they potentially are. Captive creatures in zoos and prisons are endlessly attentive to breaks in the walls or routines that may give them the slightest chance to roam beyond restraint. Farm animals live under looser strictures because much of the need for freedom has been bred out of them by genetic engineering. Pets are those rare and strange creatures who have renounced freedom and have agreed to contribute to the fulfillment of some other species. Pets occupy both ends of Pico's great chain of being, for they live both as saints and as slaves. Of the million or more species that exist, fewer than thirty have ever been willing to forego freedom in exchange for living as companions with humans. Pico knew what he was talking about when he linked freedom with dignity, but in the half-millenium since he lived we have learned that humans are not the only animals that need and enjoy those gifts.

Philosopher Ernst Cassirer summarized the effects of Pico's *Oration* which helped to transform the Medieval mind into the modern mind: Pico persuaded people to pay attention to the world rather than to the heavens as their source of knowledge, and he exalted the human ability to distinguish the self from the world. Since Pico's time, we have practiced his prescription profoundly and have absorbed its implications. Flattering though that period has been for our species, it is now evident that its half-truths are not good enough to sustain a high quality of life on Earth.

Pico's vision of human dignity has been fulfilled by generations of self-absorbed people like Pico, but only at the cost of lost dignity and freedom for powerless people and for the other creatures and processes of the Earth. Those are the wrong prices to pay. Let us declare the five hundred year experiment with modern humanism a success, but let us also declare it ended. The next step can be an affirmation that every form of life is endowed with freedom and dignity, and that the highest power rests in those who fulfill themselves without denying fulfillment to others, human or otherwise.

S. Noel c. 1988

Minding Two: Remembering

"Mind your manners" is the admonition given to one who is misbehaving, and its message is to remember what we know to be right. Behaving well on Earth expresses the profound propriety grown from centuries and millenia of experience in the contexts of natural history. Remembering probes the past in search of guidance from ancient stories, evolutionary history, and the many natural and cultural genealogies that make time meaningful, and manners mindful.

39

Earth
Stories

A ustin Hammond is a seventy-three year old elder of the Tlingit people of southeast Alaska. We met in Anchorage where we were both attending a gathering convened by Canadian Justice Thomas Berger to consider the possible future of subsistence living by native peoples of the North. If subsistence life is to continue, the lands and waters which support wildlife must remain whole and healthy. Preservation of wild lands thus is a central issue for native people.

Austin and his people have long had a running dispute with the Bureau of Land Management about ownership and management of the Chilkoot region where the Tlingits live. Austin showed how he can prove Tlingit ownership beyond a reasonable doubt. He displayed a ceremonial blanket which has been passed down for more than two hundred years in his clan. Into its fabric of mountain goat wool are woven the stories of the Tlingit people.

In song, dance, and narration, Austin told how the land was formed, how Raven made the waters, how the trees and plants came to be, how the people discovered their kinship with the sockeye salmon, and how the customs and rules governing use of the land

and waters were laid down. The stories constitute a comprehensive system which links the origins of things, the social and spiritual lives of the people, and the natural processes which surround them on their piece of the Earth. Tlingit stories are proof of Tlingit ownership in the most fundamental sense, showing how these people and this land have evolved together over thousands of years.

Where, asks Austin Hammond, are BLM's stories of the Chilkoot region? BLM has no stories to tell, but must point mutely to volumes of federal regulations, acts of congress, and court decisions, none of which is even suitable for framing, let alone usable for song, dance, or ceremony. The BLM claim seems rootless and abstract, resting upon words that wield power but fail to evoke meaning.

It must be true that people cannot claim genuine ownership of anything unless they are participants in its stories. My comfortable old easy chair is mine only because I can recall the children I have held in it, the books I have read, and the words and thoughts that have come as I sat in it. A car does not feel owned until adventures have been had in it. A house is not a home until it has accumulated a mythology of its own. Stories are a fabric into which we weave ourselves and the things that matter in our lives. They establish true ownership as sales slips and check stubs cannot, and such ownership always turns out to be a mutual affair. We are owned by what is really ours as much as we own it.

In midwinter we re-tell the basic stories of our culture. The Christmas story proves our ownership of a rich spiritual tradition, but it has nothing to say about the land we live on. The stories of western culture affirm our claim to plenty of ideas and abstract concepts, and many of them tell us how to rise above the Earth or how to pretend that it doesn't exist at all. Most of us are poor people compared to Austin Hammond, for few of our tales tell the stories that might help us to live well upon the Earth.

Why not try a little midwinter yarnspinning to lay claim to the places where we live? Along with the nativity story, children deserve to hear the stories of the nearby trees and of the birds which appear in them at different times of the year. Winter is the time to speak of the sun's annual disappearing act, and of its promised springtime reappearance. It is a good time, too, to speak of the people and animals who once lived on the land we now occupy. Good stories can celebrate our connections in time and space, as well as the ideas we live by.

Austin Hammond's blanket provides many kinds of warmth. It must feel wonderful to wrap your shoulders in wool that also tells you who you are, where you came from, and how you must live to honor your own land. Such deep coziness does not come quickly or easily, but anyone can begin to weave together the strands of the surrounding Earth into meaningful forms. There are few better ways to spend a winter.

Lizard
in the
Woodpile

I first greeted him as "Alligator lizard," then I called him "A.L.,"
and finally, Al. We met on the sun deck in front of my adobe
cottage in the desert of southern California where I was devoting a
midwinter month to a writing project. When I went out to soak up
the scarce midwinter sunshine, Al did the same on the woodpile beside
the deck. He was about eight inches long with dark olive skin whose
folds and wrinkles suggested that it didn't quite fit. Al was wary of
me at first, diving for cover at my slightest move. Gradually he realized
that I posed no threat, and he left his log to venture onto the deck.
After a few days he had established his ritual greeting, which
consisted of running one complete circle around my lounge chair
before returning to his log to stare at me and to do a few of those
odd lizardlike pushups. I spoke to him and he stared at me, and it
felt like companionship.

Both Al and I relied upon the woodpile for warmth in our different
ways. When I collected wood to burn in my stove, I found myself
avoiding the logs he favored for sunning. A log is merely a storage
vessel for solar energy, so in the end it was the sun, directly and
indirectly, that mediated my friendship with Al. His ancestors and

mine must have sought sunny places for many millenia, often sharing the same warm spots.

Al's family beat mine to the sunshine by about 85 million years. Reptiles have been around for some 280 million years, while mammals like me first showed up some 195 million years ago. Back then, Al's folks were hogging the show as dinosaurs, while we mammals scurried around at night and kept out of their way in daytime. The dinosaurs had everything their way until some unknown changes led to their extinction 64 million years ago. That's when the mammals began to proliferate. By 50 million years ago the first primates emerged, but it wasn't until around 50 thousand years ago that the first genuine humans appeared. My kind may be latecomers, but we have made heavy marks upon the Earth in our short time.

Pumping on this log, Al probably doesn't know much about his ancient pedigree. Nor has he read of the mythologies that my species has built around his kind, from snakes in the garden to fabulous dragons guarding hoards of treasure. What Al's tiny brain can't recall, however, is still stored in his genes. Deep within him lie the genetic memories of dominance and greatness, ready to respond whenever the Earth sends signals that it is his time again.

Sometimes I wonder what it must feel like to be a modern resident of Athens, and to go about daily affairs amidst constant reminders of the glories achieved by one's ancestors of 2500 years ago. Selling insurance in the shadow of the Acropolis must seem like a shallow substitute. Americans can feel something of that during lackluster election years as we listen to the meager fare that is offered us and wonder whatever became of quality mind and character like that found in Jefferson, Lincoln, and other great leaders of our past. Like Al the Lizard, we all have to wait through periods of emptiness, knowing that somewhere deep within us lies the capacity for more abundant and genuine life.

While we wait, Al and I can still enjoy one another's company and the shared sunlight. Both of us carry within us the accumulated experience of all those who have lived and died before us, and both of us have the capacity to become more complete in the future than we are now. Al seems to be patient, and I try to be patient, too. What better can we do than enjoy one another's companionship, revel in the sunshine, and wait for the next step?

Bear
Bearings

N avigators who want to find their bearings often look to the north star and to its flanking constellations, *Ursa major* and *Ursa minor*, the great bears in the sky. The stately procession of bears around the apex of the sky has helped to orient humans in time and space and spirit for as long as there have been people to look upward. Bears are still there in the sky, here on Earth, and underground in caves as guides to bearable and sensitive living, but most of us have forgotten how to read their messages.

Remembering bears has been a research effort of my friend Paul Shepard for more than a decade. Paul and I have talked bears for years, and he has published many of his thoughts about bears with Barry Sanders in their book, *The Sacred Paw* (New York, Viking Press, 1985). Recalling bears takes more than a little head-scratching, for their story in human consciousness precedes agriculture and civilization, and begins with the seeds of human self-awareness. When people first became acquainted with themselves, it was with the help of bears.

Like humans, bears are omnivorous. Since most everything is potential food to them, everything in the world is interesting and worthy of close attention. Curiosity and intelligent appraisal of surroundings are obvious similarities between the two species. Bears stand erect, use their arms as weapons and to solve problems, and sit frumpily on their bottoms as people do. Bear mothers are expert parents who nurture, love, and educate their cubs toward competent independence. Women bear children, children bear watching: these verbs in our language are not accidental.

Birth connects people to bears, but so does death. When the year dies in autumn, the bear enters its cave in the earth for hibernation. Apparent death is an annual event for bears as their bodily processes slow and they excuse themselves from the daily round of hunting, eating, excreting. Females bear their young during the winter and nourish them in the darkness. When spring comes, bears seem to overcome death and to re-emerge in the company of new life. They were probably the first examples people ever saw of creatures resembling themselves who could experience transformation, renewal, and resurrection.

Before there was an Earth Mother in human thought, the Bear Mother was there to represent the kinship of humans and nature. Bear Mother's story, told in many cultures over thousands of years, shows that "both bears and people are part animal, part human," and that mutual respect grows from recognition of their common origins. Shepard and Sanders believe that the Bear Mother may have been "the first great mythopoetic mother of all life (the first external incarnation among animals of our personal mothers), prior in history and deeper in the psyche than her humanlike expressions, the goddesses and madonnas of civilization." The Earth Mother appears later with the advent of agriculture, and goddesses are still later specialists.

The caves of bears were early symbols suggesting both the womb that brings forth new life, and the grave that awaits all living beings. *The Sacred Paw* examines funeral ceremonies from 50,000 years ago in which the remains of bears and humans were treated with the same care and the same ritual placements. More modern evidence from recent or existing hunting peoples demonstrates similar themes, attitudes, and practices. The authors conclude that "the bear was both metaphor in its hibernation cycle and ritual instrument in the earliest human funerary practices." The lore of bears is the oldest evidence on Earth for human spirituality.

Literature preserves the symbolism of bears even in cultures where the animals themselves are unknown. Homer's *Odyssey* is the transformed story of the son of a bear. The Greek goddess Artemis was once a Bear Mother who was later transformed into a huntress and a protector of wilderness. The stories of King Arthur (from the Greek *arktos,* bear) are filled with bearish signs, no doubt transformed from much earlier tales. William Faulkner's *The Bear* is only one of the modern stories which repeat ancient patterns in continually renewed settings. The visit of Goldilocks to a bear family still delights children and teaches them its lessons, as does Winnie the Pooh. And millions of us have gone to sleep with a teddy bear that gives both comfort and assurance that a new day is coming.

Although bears are as active as ever in the human imagination, their numbers continue to shrink in the wild. In habitats where bears and humans once shared space, humans now live with only their own kind to instruct them. Modern people are torn between their love of bear symbols and stories and their fear of real bears. As Gary Snyder says in his postscript to *The Sacred Paw,* what people really fear about bears is the idea of bears: "the unseen, dark forces that lurk in the forest of our mind." Both bears and forests are eliminated by people who search for power, comfort, ease, and safety, perhaps without understanding that their own minds and spirits are diminished in the process.

A world without bears would be a diminished place for people, but that will never happen. Bear habitats may be destroyed and the last bears on Earth may one day disappear, but the Bear Mother and her many progeny will still wield their powers deep in the caves of the human mind.

Humbugs
and
Bugbears

Dickens' Scrooge made it fashionable to say "humbug" at Christmastime, but linguists say the term had been around for a century before Dickens came along. They also say humbug (meaning sham, hypocrisy) probably derived from "hem and haw" (stalling) or possibly from "bugbear" (bogey or goblin). No one says how bugs or bears got involved in all this nasty stuff. The ancient root for "bear" simply means "the brown animal," with no moral judgment implied.

Somewhere along the line humans began dumping their negative feelings upon animals, building into language subtle biases against creatures who undeservedly became symbols for human vices and fears. Maybe it began with that hapless snake in the Garden of Eden. Whatever the origins, we have accumulated a huge vocabulary that suggests human estrangement from other animals and conveys faulty views of what they really mean to us.

And what do they mean to us? We are just now rediscovering through science what our ancient ancestors knew well when they named "the brown animal." Ecology is reminding us that life is an intricate web of earth, plants, and animals, and that all have a right to participate in natural processes. Mistakes of human judgment made in recent centuries have torn the web badly through destruction of habitats, extinction of species, and poisoning of the essential elements that make life possible. Awareness is growing that the life of animals is also our life. Without a healthy natural world, human language, civilization, and spirit cannot persist.

Every Christmas brings plenty of sham and hypocrisy, but it also carries a promise of renewal and a fresh hope that things can get better. Every Scrooge can change his life quickly once he experiences a vision that changes his perspectives about what is important. Bugs and bears are important, and along with all the other creatures on this planet, they share the gift of life which must be the foundation for our visions of the future.

Heard
From
the Birds

Whether they spoke or not is conjectural, but I heard from two birds last summer. The messages were important, although it is not easy to say just what their content was. It had to do with celebration.

The messages came about a week apart. Both were heard along the banks of the upper Rogue River in Oregon's Cascade Mountains, where my family has had a small cabin for some thirty years. It is a quiet place with mature Douglas firs and sugar pines above an understory of dense vine maples, dogwoods, berries, and many miniature plants. Inch by inch, I have known and loved that place intimately for most of my life.

There is a spot on the river bank where we draw pails of water for our plumbing-free cabin. It is also where we scattered the ashes of my brother George after his death a few years ago. I was sitting there alone this summer, listening to the river ripple and thinking of George, when a water ouzel took flight from the grasses near my feet and sang its joyous high-pitched song until it disappeared upstream. The ouzel has always seemed a comical little bird to me, with its constant bobbing dance and endless self-important chattering. I find it impossible to watch ouzels without smiling, and this one lightened my spirit when it needed lightening.

It is not new to associate birds with spirits. Every mythology, ancient and recent, has done so. Birds draw our eyes and our feelings upwards, and their songs are our most basic music. As far back in time as human stories go, birds have lightly borne the spirits of dead and living people, just as this water ouzel did for my brother and me.

My next message came at dawn as I was walking the river path to clear my head of a deep sleep. At a bend in the river there is a small sandy beach where we swim on hot August days. There on the gravel bar was a bird I have never before seen in such a place: a great blue heron. The heron flew ponderously, soundlessly, gracefully when it saw me, but only to the limb of a nearby dead fir. I sat still on a downed log, and soon it returned. For the next hour we watched one another while the river flowed between us. Neither of us did anything at all; we just looked at one another. For me, that hour was a gift. The day happened to be my birthday.

Not for a minute do I pretend that the ouzel was mindful of my brother or the heron of my birthday. Birds have more important things to do than to concern themselves with the inner lives of humans. In another culture or at another time, I might have read omens from these encounters, or found a priest or shaman to interpret them to me. But my world has not taught me that birds are messengers from gods and spirits, and so I share the pseudo-scientific view of my time that they are interesting natural creatures, products of evolutionary history, answerable only to the ecological niches they inhabit.

Although this heron was out of its normal lowland marshy niche and visiting a rushing mountain stream, there is still no great cause for wonder. Herons eat fish, and their broad wings can take them wherever fish are, marsh or mountains. Of course, this heron wasn't fishing, and it does seem a little odd that in thirty years of river-watching I have never seen one there, nor do I know of anyone else who has. But let it go; herons have their lives, and I have mine.

Yet, the heron, the ouzel, and I touched for a moment, and our touching seemed good and important. There was no resemblance to the meetings with jays who come demanding handouts, or to those city birds who cast a deferential and cautious glance from the fencetop bird feeder. These encounters bore meaning. The difference must lie in the natural setting where these meetings took place, and in the feelings such settings engender in willing people. It is easy to believe that I am a different person beside a rushing river than I am beside a speeding city street. The river person is more likely to find significance than threats in unexpected happenings, and more likely to interpret the meaning of events than simply to assess their practical consequences.

Birds seem to find ways to be almost everywhere, even cities. They and the rodents and insects are wild animals who insist upon earning their livings amongst us in spite of pavement and all that goes with it. We need more meaningful contact with these creatures. There must be ways to nourish and liberate the river people who lie within each of us, whatever the settings. It requires listening for clues to the meanings of life by attending to its many forms, patterns, and surprises. Wherever we are, we can celebrate with the birds and listen to them, whether they speak or not.

Nuclear
Time

S piritual traditions worldwide agree upon a couple of principles: the origins of things are sacred, and what is sacred is always dangerous. Creation stories and accounts of frightening encounters with deities affirm these principles from widely divergent cultures and periods of time, suggesting that they represent fundamental human attitudes toward the cosmos we live in. The powers and dangers of origins are present in modern feelings about nuclear energy.

How far back in time do we need to go to find energy sources? The wood I burn to heat my home has mostly grown during my lifetime, as the trees around me have stored some of the same solar energy that also shines on me. When I burn coal, oil products, or natural gas, I am drawing upon their cambrian origins some 600 million years ago. If I choose to add nuclear energy to my repertoire, I am dipping deeply into the time before the origin of the solar system when energy was stored in atomic nuclei. The farther back in time I go for my energy, the scarier it gets.

Much effort has gone into making the development of nuclear energy seem a thoroughly profane affair, useful to make weapons and to power machines, but without spiritual content. Sanitary-looking facilities are built to confine bizarre forces at work within them, and it all looks like a tidy technology under human control. Now and then, however, the meaning of nuclear energy peeks out from a Three Mile Island or a Chernobyl to confront us with the origins of the universe and the terrors of ultimate forces. Our spirits are moved, not just our minds, when we are reminded that containment buildings are not enough to restrain the original powers of creation and death.

The tree dies, too, before I burn it to release its energy, and that process also has spiritual content. But the tree and I are contemporaries who understand one another, and each of us can be nourished by the death of the other. When energy comes from sources billions of years distant in time, then I enter a cosmic context where life and its needs are insignificant, and the trees and I don't count. That godlike perspective is beyond me, and I fear its dangers. Let me burn the friendly wood, and live within my own time.

Nathan
and
the Utes

The power and prestige of the United States was challenged by
a few people from another culture with a long history of warlike
enthusiasm. Senseless murders had happened and hostages had been
taken to an unknown location. The President of the United States
made threatening and heroic pronouncements, and the news media
carried these alongside soul-wrenching interviews with witnesses and
survivors. Military forces moved in ready for a strike. A respected
leader with influence over the kidnappers helped to negotiate the
eventual release of the hostages. Then the consequences began to
unfold. All of that happened in September, 1879, in Colorado.

The warriors were Ute Indians, who were then a sovereign people
owning twelve million acres on the west slope of the Colorado
Rockies. They were American citizens under the Fourteenth
Amendment to the Constitution, and their perpetual rights were
guaranteed by Acts of Congress. The White River Utes, hunters and
devoted horsemen, had never been at war with white settlers, and
had never before that day killed a white person. Their Chief was
Ouray, widely recognized as a wise and powerful leader and a man

of peace. The Utes loved their mountains, their swift horses, and their wide-ranging way of life. They had little interest in agriculture or in the white civilization that came with it.

Enter my distant relative Nathan Meeker. Nathan was an educated idealist, a writer of adventure novels, and a Civil War reporter for Horace Greeley's *New York Tribune*. He heeded Greeley's advice to "Go West, young man," and founded the Utopian community of Greeley, Colorado. Then when the opportunity came to bring the glories of civilization to the White River Utes as Indian Agent, he could not resist. With the enthusiasm of a man who knew that inevitability was on his side, Nathan persuaded and coerced the Utes to try farming, fully convinced that he was creating an alternative future where peace and prosperity would reign for all.

Ponies were symbols of freedom to the Utes, but to Nathan Meeker they stood for the irresponsibility that prevented successful farming. He knew he was going to the heart of the matter when he ordered that plowing begin on the race track where young Utes competed in horsemanship. A deep-seated Ute cultural button was unwittingly pushed by Nathan, and the Utes instantly became warriors with a purpose and an enemy. Reasons and futures suddenly became irrelevant. When the dust cleared, the Agency employees were dead, the women had been kidnapped, and Nathan Meeker was found with a bullet hole in his head, a chain around his neck by which he had been dragged by Ute ponies, and a barrel stave shoved down his throat. The Utes knew about symbols.

The nation was outraged and clamored for revenge. The army came in force. Chief Ouray, who had not been involved in the massacre, forbade further fighting by Utes and helped to negotiate the release of the women hostages who had been held for three weeks. Politicians campaigned on their plans to teach the Indians a lesson and, incidentally, to appropriate their rich lands for agricultural and mineral development. Within a year, title to all Ute lands was extinguished, their treaty rights were cancelled, and they had been moved at gunpoint to land no one wanted in Utah. The whole sad story is well told in Marshall Sprague's book, *Massacre* (Lincoln, University of Nebraska Press).

The violence at White River is much easier to understand in retrospect than it was a century ago. Two cultures with radically different values and emotional patterns collided over land-use issues and the lifestyles that accompany them. The Ute way of subsistence living on wild land lost, as usual, to the American passion for agricultural and commercial development. The people who made that decision, Utes and whites alike, did not know quite what they were doing, but acted from the fears and frenzies of the moment which were nevertheless rooted in deep cultural traditions.

When cultures clash and passions rise to violent states, terror makes decisions that inevitably damage both people and the Earth. News of such crazy behavior causes anguish in all who hear it, whether the dispatches come from White River in 1879 or from Beirut today. Hatred replaces understanding, and all sense of context and consequence disappears beneath escalating acts of revenge. That can go on for centuries as it has in the Middle East, in Africa, in Ireland, and in America today. The scale of violence has increased because of the weapons available, but the impulses which create terrorism are as ancient as the human species.

The incident at White River involved only a handful of people. Twelve Utes were arrested, but none was ever charged or brought to trial. It would have seemed almost trivial if it had not involved a well-known figure like Nathan Meeker, and if it had not come at a time when thousands of settlers and miners were itching to get their hands on Ute land. A few people in an obscure place acting madly for a few hours made national headlines and changed the future for millions of people and millions of acres. Historians call it the last major military confrontation between Indians and whites. But it was not the last time that impassioned terrorism will shape the future.

Epistle:
William Meeker
(Ca. 1620-1690)

Dear William:

There is little more than a shared name to link us over the
nearly four centuries that separate us. Maybe a couple of genes
have survived the dilution of some fourteen generations between you
and me, but our family resemblance is probably pretty slim. Somehow
you sit rather solidly at the beginning of my American family tree,
and I like having you there. I also envy you for having seen America
before it became what it now is.

They say you arrived here in 1635 aboard the sailing ship "True
Love" from England. Shortly after that, there is word that you helped
to negotiate the purchase of the site for Elizabethtown, New Jersey,
from its Indian residents. There is no mention of price, nor whether
the Indians knew or cared what real estate deals were all about. When
the town was established, you became its constable. I like the one
thing that is recorded about your constabulary: you were indicted in
behalf of King Charles II for "riotous conduct," evidently because
you tore down a fence that someone had erected on the town
commons. You're my kind of ancestor, William.

Your town, Elizabeth, is today a smoldering collection of factories
and refineries with lots of grimy concrete and precious little land

showing. It does scant honor to the queen you named it for. If you were to visit there you could not find your way around, and most likely you could not find a single natural feature that looked familiar. You would be terrified in that strange place, gassed by its fumes and run down by its traffic. If you first came to America in order to get away from misery in England, you would find that environments of misery have been replicated several times over in New Jersey since then.

I live on the west coast of the continent that you helped to colonize. Only for the past century and a half have people defaced this land, so it is not as lost as New Jersey is. But if there should be some future Meeker three hundred years hence to muse upon me as I am musing upon you, he may feel as sad about California as I do about New Jersey.

Someone in the family has researched our geneology and drawn up a family tree that almost connects you and me. There are gaps, perhaps left by some of your descendants whose lives were either too obscure or too disreputable to be noted in public records. Those who appear have left precious little: they were born, married, had children, and died. Four lines will accommodate all I know about them. Sometimes the place of their death was farther west than the place of their birth, which I suppose is how I got to the west coast after you began in the east.

There is also a computer printout of all the Meekers now listed in United States phone books. Presumably most of them are there thanks to you, William. Their number totals about three thousand, enough for a good-sized town, and probably more than the total white population of North America when you arrived here. We have been fruitful and multiplied, which is just what your Puritan preachers used to command you to do.

So between us, dear William, we have bartered and stolen this land from the Indians, spanned it from one shore to the other, populated it to the limits, converted much of it from beautiful cheap land to ugly expensive land, and depleted its goods. So far as I can tell, none of us meant any harm. Why am I not more proud of us?

Love, Joe

Epistle:
Louis Pasteur
(1822-1895)

Dear Louis:

Your name is on every milk carton these days because of your deep compassion for human suffering. You made it possible for your successors to pasteurize much of the world, and they have done so. Thank you, I think.

When educators need an example to show how science serves the needs of humanity, you are about the best there is. Selflessly, you used your great scientific talents to find out why so many children and innocents were dying from the foods they ate. You founded bacteriology, and developed the technology to apply it to food processing in order to prevent diseases and to save lives. Thanks to you, millions who would otherwise have suffered and died have been able instead to live normal, healthy lives. I don't think you even benefitted from the patents that flowed from your work, but humanity has expressed its gratitude in other ways. You are a hero.

If bacteria had heroes, they would be humbled before you. They were doing so well, extending their influence and colonizing new territories, and you wiped them out by the billions. Bacteria still struggle to recover the human places you banished them from, and they show much inventiveness in finding fresh approaches and new forms that will sidestep your defenses. But your scientific heirs are carrying on your battle, and so far the bacteria remain mostly at bay.

There were some consequences of your work that you might not have envisioned. Food preservation has become big business, and now there is scarcely anything people eat that has not been treated with some chemical or thermal process to control the bugs that want it as much as we do. Foods are less tasty, less nutritious, and often downright dangerous as a result. You are also the grandfather of junk foods which numb our tummies and our minds. More significantly, those lives you saved have been enthusiastically reproducing themselves, creating a human population explosion which seriously overtakes the Earth's capacity and strains all modern social structures. There is much suffering in the world because of you, and more to come.

There is a Chinese saying, Taoist no doubt, that says "he who serves humanity destroys the Earth." Even though your intentions were the best and your love was as pure as your science, Louis, your life is also an example of what the Chinese had in mind.

Best Wishes,
Joe

Epistle:
Ebenezer Scrooge
(1843-Present)

Dear Ebenezer:

Charles Dickens was unfair to you. He provided you with a name contrived to frighten little children. He told your story from the biased perspective of a middle class Victorian working family. He even made you seem vaguely responsible for the sufferings of a handicapped child, to whom he gave, of course, the endearing name of Tiny Tim. Every deft Dickensian brushstroke created sentiment against you, and each led inevitably toward your climactic transformation into a loving, lovable, renewed spirit of Christmas.

Today we know you better for what you are: a harried, aging, urban professional in a state of personal crisis. Partners and friends have slipped away, and the sound business practices that once defined the good life now fail to arouse your vigor as they once did. Your firm needs organizational development, and you could use a therapist.

There are pills available to prevent the bad dreams you are visited by. Those dreams are heavy with moral judgments, anyway, and we have learned that it is better to live without such burdens. Guilt over the past, disgust with the present, and fears of the future are emotions that healthy people do not need. We have also learned that it is more or less normal to feel some midwinter depression, especially at Christmastime. It would be a good idea to have your name changed to something cheerier. Perhaps you should also exercise more, and change your diet.

As Dickens presented you, you were a sad product of commercial culture. Business had bled the humanity and compassion from you, he thought, but in his affirmative way he showed that you could be made into a good fellow again by viewing the origins and consequences of your life through the spirits of Christmasses Past, Present, and Future. What Dickens didn't know was that you simply lacked good role models. Living under the reign of a lady like Victoria, how could you have guessed that it is possible to retain your hard-headed values and still seem like a nice guy in public? A good public relations consultant and some tasteful media exposure can now turn a man like you into an inspiring model of success.

There are still moralists like Dickens among us who grouse that Christmas isn't what it used to be. When we look back at your Christmas of 1843, we can see that they are wrong. It is still commercial, still difficult for disabled and deprived people, still a time of anxiety, and still filled with spirits that inspire change and renewal. You may be better prepared to resist them now than you were a century and a half ago, but you will have to be careful for the spirits, too, have learned some new tricks. Some people today are listening to the spirits through the natural places where they live, such as forests where evergreen trees speak their continual message of renewal. So you should be especially on your guard if your Christmas tree tries to tell you where it came from, and what it means.

Bless you, Ebenezer, and us all, every one.

Cheers,
Joe

Minding Three: Caring

Minding means caring for, as when one is charged to "mind the shop."
It sounds a little like stewardship, for the minder of a shop could be
merely an agent for an absent owner. But the Earth is nobody's shop, and
management is not our best role in its affairs. Earth-minding calls
for attentiveness to life, respect for the integrity of its processes, and
responsible thought and action. Healthy minding is caring participation with
the Earth.

Making Tracks

A s the story goes, Aristippus, a Socratic philosopher, was
shipwrecked on the Isle of Rhodes. When he found geometrical
figures in the sand, Aristippus cried out to his fellow survivors, "Let
us be of good hope, for indeed I see the traces of men." The story
seemed significant to the Roman architect Vitruvius, who told it in
De architectura, a book that has influenced the way people build things
for the past two thousand years. It was significant in other ways to
Clarence Glacken, the modern geographer who wrote a monu-
mental study of human-nature relationships called *Traces on the
Rhodian Shore* (Berkeley, U.C. Press, 1967). A big chunk of Western
history has been devoted to speculations about how people should
draw their lines upon the Earth.

Uneasily, I participate in this vast tradition as I plan and clear a
walking trail through the forest where I live. This forest is scarcely
virgin; half a century ago the mature cedars that stood here were
clearcut. Their stumps, three to five feet in diameter and spaced
forty to fifty feet apart, make it possible to squint a little and
envision the former cedar forest in its prime. Rotten posts and bits
of rusted wire tell of the next period when cattle grazed on this stump

ranch. But trees in this climate are persistent, and soon they were again abundant enough to make grazing impractical. So the people moved on and the forest went about its business.

Now it is a jumble of second-growth trees with a dense understory of ferns, berries and shrubs. The pioneering alders are gradually being outclassed by hemlocks and firs more than one hundred feet tall. Madrones grow that high, too, with their lanky trunks supporting an umbrella of leaves competing for the sunlight. Here and there are vigorous young cedars, vestiges of the past with the eventual future of this forest implicit in them. The cedars will rise again.

Meanwhile, I want to walk in the forest, and for that I need a trail. The deer don't, but their feet are daintier and their footing surer than mine. Like the deer, I need not travel in straight lines with my trail. It is a principle of forest life that straight lines do not exist. So the trail meanders, cleared of twigs and branches, but going out of its way to avoid larger logs. It rises and falls with the uneven forest floor, and its surface is a bed of soft needles. Sprouts of holly and hemlock grow in it, but they are easily stepped around. When salal bushes or berry vines invade the trail too vigorously, they get pruned.

It is a minimum trail, but like those geometrical marks seen by Aristippus, it declares that people are nearby. No apology is needed, for this forest is my home as rightly as it is the home for the deer, the raccoons, and the trees. The trail is my habitual route through my habitat, made by a species that seems culturally committed to such scribbling upon the Earth's surface. Accepting that, the best I can do is to assure that my scribblings will be light and easily erased. Within a year after I stop tending the trail, no one will be able to find it.

As I walk the trial, the forest is making tracks upon me that will not be easily erased. If I am attentive and careful, I can learn and grow toward maturity along with the trees. My species has done so for many millenia in forests like this, learning what we must do to become whole people from our interactions with whole natural systems.

A good friend and a fine artist, Gilah Yelin Hirsch, has been investigating a subject she calls *cosmography*, or "the writing of the universe." Her guess is that human alphabets and fundamental visual images have arisen by imitation of natural forms found repeatedly in wilderness settings. She has documented hundreds of correspondences between ancient Semitic and Oriental languages and consistent forms of vegetation, patterns in rocks and water, and landforms. If Gilah is right, the universe has been quite literally writing upon humans for many thousands of years, and our alphabets are among the trails that nature has carved in order to cross our minds.

Wild lands have cut deeper trails in my life than I will ever be able to make in the forest. It is also true that I and my kind have abused and decimated wilderness, often irretrievably. We have censored and edited cosmography, the writing of the universe, until it is beyond recognition and all but mute in many human lives. But perhaps we can revise old Aristippus and remember to be of good hope, for indeed we can see the traces of wilderness within us.

Irony
Deficiency

During a political year, everyone seems to become insufferably earnest. We are treated to an array of grave dangers, glorious prospects, and grim reality by candidates whose moral superiority is as inflated as their windy rhetoric. They are not trying so much to persuade us with good reasons, as to smother us with shallow emotions. It is a national orgy of kitsch.

Kitsch is a German word for trashy art of no esthetic importance. The contemporary Czech author, Milan Kundera, took kitsch as a major theme in his novel, *The Unbearable Lightness of Being*. Kundera finds that kitsch has passed far beyond the borders of poor but popular art, and now permeates social and political life at all levels. Kitsch has become the morality of the modern multitude.

Characteristics of kitsch include emotional simplicity, a concern for style that ignores substance, a capacity to be grasped instantly by almost everyone, and an absence of complexity or humor. Kundera's prime example of political kitsch is the ritual of the Grand March on May Day, imposed upon his Czech homeland since the Communist takeover: "The Grand March is the splended march on the road to brotherhood, equality, justice, happiness; it goes on and on, obstacles notwithstanding." The daily reality which fails to display these noble ideals is forgotten as people join together in a common spectacle of unreality. This is kitsch, a collective euphoria that Kundera calls "the dictatorship of the heart."

Political platforms are built with planks of seasoned kitsch, but so are the ideals of many modern social movements and commercial enterprises. Popular psychologies, food fads, and health movements march under banners of kitsch. It is kitsch that makes possible the unquestioned devotion to a favorite football or baseball team. Without kitsch, sales of pharmaceuticals and new cars would plummet. Kitsch is the emotional hook that we swallow readily because it seems that everyone is doing it, and because kitsch is so sincere.

There is also environmental kitsch. Cute baby animals tug at public sentiments to gain support for wildlife protection. Dramatic sunsets and wilderness vistas convey the peacefulness and purity of nature, and persuade millions to join environmental organizations. Some have scornfully dubbed such kinds of environmentalism "shallow ecology" to distinguish it from the "deep ecology" which addresses fundamental values of human culture as they relate to natural systems. There is some danger in such distinctions, for as Milan Kundera reminds us, "no matter how we scorn it, kitsch is an integral part of the human condition." Scorn is merely the snobbish side of the kitsch coin, while the front side is sentiment.

Neither sentiment nor scorn is a good guide for thought and action, though both will be with us always. What they both lack is irony, the vision which sees the world from several perspectives at once, and smiles at the discontinuities and contradictions of life on Earth. Irony can penetrate the thin veil of illusion that kitsch casts upon experience to reveal the multiple realities that hide behind Grand Marches, presidential politics, TV commercials, and environmental enthusiasms. Once we perceive that the bearers of kitsch are playacting in public, it is much easier to be free of their emotional influence.

Kitsch is eternal, built solidly into the limbic levels of the human brain through eons of evolution. Its mild and pleasant emotions are associated with things that seem cute or pretty or picturesque, and its experiences promote group solidarity, conventional morality, fashions and fads, and shallow patriotism. The ordinary sentiments of kitsch link us together with feelings of belonging. Masters of media in our time have learned to manipulate kitschy levels of our emotional lives in order to sell us products, unneeded services, shallow entertainments, and political candidates.

Irony lives in another ancient part of the brain along with playfulness, laughter, and the capacity to notice that nothing is as simple as sentiment says it is. We feel it in music that expresses counterpoints of harmony and rhythm, and in melodies that seem to leave something unsaid. Ironies of language convey multiple meanings simultaneously, as in the title of this essay. And there are ironies of public judgment, such as the belief that automobiles would create clean and healthful cities by replacing horses and their curbside droppings. Irony looks upon things with a wry smile, always aware that kitschy sentiments conceal important implications.

Susceptibility to kitsch may be caused by irony deficiency. Since no one knows quite how to measure irony, it is difficult to establish a recommended daily amount, but I think it safe to say that no day is complete without a good dose or two of irony. It is especially recommended while watching television, or when ideological salesmen knock at the door. And it is the only antidote I know that will help us to survive the earnestness of political posturing.

Assisi
and the
Stewards

Historian Lynn White, Jr., was one of the first to see clearly that ecology raises spiritual questions and that it challenges widely held ethical ideas. His 1967 article in *Science*, "The Historical Roots of Our Ecologic Crisis," argued that Christianity and its value system bear major responsibility for the destructive exploitation of nature. By declaring that humanity has an effective monopoly on spirit in this world, White argued, Christianity has devalued all natural creation and made nature subject to human dominion for any and all human purposes. White's article was reprinted in scores of environmental books during the 1970's, for it was one of the rare documents to address religious questions raised by ecological problems.

Christian churches were distressed to find their faith blamed for the degradation of nature, and began looking for ways to respond to the accusations of Lynn White, and of the many young environmentalists influenced by him. Many Christians decided then that human dominion over nature, as mentioned in Chapter 1 of Genesis, seemed rather too aggressive, and that it would be better to emphasize the idea of stewardship, alluded to in Genesis 2. Humanity was henceforth to be regarded as God's steward, a responsible governor placed on Earth to tend and keep it in good shape in the absence of its true owner. The idea caught on and soon won the support of most religious leaders and many scientists, and has since become a key concept for many modern environmental groups. "Stewardship of the Earth" is a vision of benevolent, non-violent management, enlightened by science, and intended to create a garden-like Earth where all creatures will thrive in peace.

Stewardship, as such, is not mentioned in the Bible, but comes from medieval sources. The Old English word *stiweard* designated "the warden of the sty," or the pig-keeper. Steward proved to be an upwardly-mobile word, and soon attained its modern meaning as "a person who manages another's property, or who administers anything as the agent of another." It has also been used to designate people who tend to the domestic needs of passengers on vessels and airplanes. Airline stewardesses recently objected to being thought of as wardens of their sties in the skies, and are now known as flight attendants. But religious and environmental groups still love the idea of steward-ship, and have further elevated its status to include benevolent management of the entire planet.

Stewardship was a prominent theme at a conference of world religions sponsored by the World Wide Fund for Nature in 1986 at the Basilica of St. Francis of Assisi. WWF arranged the meeting to promote cooperation between conservation and religion, and to clarify the beliefs of major world religions concerning the ecology of the Earth. The five largest world religions—Buddhism, Christianity, Hinduism, Islam, and Judaism—were all represented, along with many spokespersons from other religious groups. WWF hoped that a unified statement on religion and ecology might emerge, but that soon proved to be impossible. Instead, each religion offered its own perspec-tive on the relationship between mankind and nature, and these have since been published as *The Assisi Declarations*. The *Declarations* show that for three of the five major world religions, images of human power and authority are dominant, and the main theme is stewardship. For two others, nature itself has spiritual qualities in which humanity participates, and the idea of stewardship does not appear.

The Christian statement identifies God as a Father who made all things as gifts for his children, humanity. These children are "kings of all upon earth, but subject to heaven." Humanity's regal dominion, in this modern interpretation, is seen now as "steward-ship in symbiosis with all creatures." Symbiotic stewardship may sound like a contradiction in terms, but it is evidently invoked to convey an image of mutual dependency between humanity and nature while leaving no doubt that people are in charge. Stewardship in symbiosis must be something like despotism in democracy, which shouldn't be too hard for the modern mind to recognize. The lines of human power and authority remain clear, yet there is recognition that all creatures share the same real estate. The duty of Christians, then, is to repudiate "all ill-considered exploitation of nature which threatens to destroy it and, in turn, to make man the victim of degradation." Christian stewards are supposed to keep healthy habitats.

The Muslim declaration seems more legal and businesslike. Property rights are established immediately with the assertion that "the universe belongs to God, its maker." Humanity exists on Earth only in the role of *Khalifa* (diminuitive of Caliph), a viceregent or trustee of God: "We are God's stewards and agents on Earth." As overseers of God's property in trust, humans are to be held account-able at a future day of Reckoning (*akrah*). The main purpose of Islam is to provide guidance so that people can face *akrah* when it comes. Muhammed, the Prophet of Islam, gave instructions concerning the planting and tending of fruit trees, and endorsed the charity of providing food from the fields for "men and beasts and birds." It was also a Muslim jurist of the thirteenth century who formulated the first bill of legal rights for domestic animals. Muslim trustees of nature, we are told, "draw up the right balance sheet of possibilities, and properly weigh the environmental costs and benefits of what we want." Islamic stewards are expected to manage God's property well, or face the consequences.

74

"Whoever is merciful to all creatures is a descendent of our ancestor Abraham," begins the Jewish declaration on nature. Merciful management is its theme, beginning with Adam who was placed in the Garden of Eden "to tend and guard it." (Genesis 2:15) Adam also named all creatures, thus defining their essence. He then "accepted responsibility before God for all creation." and assumed his role as "leader and custodian of the natural world." Power and good stewardship are sometimes in conflict, but this tension may be resolved by behaving towards the rest of creation with justice and compassion. An example is the Talmudic teaching on vegetarianism, which affirms "the autonomy of all living creatures." The final Jewish image of mankind on Earth likens the planet to a rowboat which no one has a right to scuttle: "Let us safeguard our rowboat," says the Jewish declaration about nature, "and let us row together."

However green and compassionate may be the language of these three religions, their concepts of stewardship emphasize the power and dominance of humanity. These stewards are kings, managers, pilots, and executive officers who serve as benevolent bosses of the natural world for its absentee landlord. All specific references to nature in their statements are to domesticated plants and animals and to habitats used for human benefit. Wilderness has no place in their thinking, and there is no intrinsic value in the nature they speak of. The Oriental religions represented in the *Declarations* tell a different story.

The Vedas, ancient hymns of the Hindu faith, celebrate "all objects in the universe, living or non-living, as being pervaded by the same spiritual power." The Hindu view of divinity sees it as a pervasive force "manifesting itself in a graded scale of evolution." Humans seem to occupy a favored role in evolution "at present," but that may change without disturbing the spiritual welfare of the cosmos. Reverence for life requires attentiveness to all of nature, for "the divine is not exterior to creation, but expresses itself through natural phenomena." Evolution, the Hindu spokesman says, is "a series of divine incarnations" in which spiritual life develops through

75

the emergence of new species. Thus, "man did not spring fully formed to dominate lesser lifeforms, but rather evolved out of these forms itself, and is therefore integrally linked to the rest of creation." Conservation of nature, to the Hindus, is a spiritual necessity of the highest order, for the Earth is "the Universal Mother."

The Buddhist declaration begins with homage to the Buddha, "who saw the interdependence of Nature, and taught it to the world." The karma that causes suffering or happiness among humans operates equally for all other living creatures, and the teachings of Buddhism seek to create "light and happiness for all sentient beings." Usefulness to humanity is not among the criteria for evaluating nature, for utility can be used to justify misuse by the powerful of both nature and humans. Besides, the Buddhist theory of continuous rebirth implies that many non-human creatures have souls that were formerly human. Spirit is everywhere, "in the rivers, mountains, lakes, and trees," and it must be revered as fully as human spirit in the Buddhist view.

Five brief statements by representatives of major world religions cannot adequately convey the environmental theologies of these traditions. Nor can they truly reflect the ways in which these religions have affected the parts of the Earth where they are practiced. Bleak environmental disasters are to be found in the shadows of each belief, as are glorious triumphs of wilderness conservation. Belief is one thing, behavior another. But since conservation is fashionable for the first time in the past few thousand years, each religion predictably proclaims itself the founder of all environmental ethics. These five declarations cannot tell us which religion is most responsible for environmental destruction, or which can best help to heal the Earth.

The declarations do raise basic questions, however, that everyone interested in conservation needs to consider: is conservation a spiritual matter, and is the Earth a spiritual being? If humanity has an exclusive corner on spirit, as Christianity, Judaism, and Islam agree, then people are stewards, managers, and custodians of a purely material creation. Their world is essentially a farm, with priority given to domesticated plants and animals used by people. Human power and control determine the destiny of all creatures, and the best we can do is to try to exercise stewardly functions with good knowledge, careful thinking, and loving responsibility over an Earth that consists of raw materials. Western conservation groups and western religions have usually agreed that the earth is a human possession held in trust, and is to be managed for human benefit.

But if spirit is pervasive throughout nature, shared by all that lives, then the human role may be that of a participant, not a manager. This is the implication of the messages from Hinduism and Buddhism, and from most of the world's aboriginal religions. These voices have been strengthened recently by western scientists exploring the possibility that the Earth is a living creature (the Gaia hypothesis), by the "deep ecology" movement, by women's groups looking for the natural foundations of women's spirituality, by legal and philosophical speculations on the rights of non-human nature, and by some adherents of green politics. This growing chorus has not yet found a clear voice, but its murmurings assert that the Earth and all its creatures are part of a total cosmic reality that is spiritually alive through all of its participants. This emerging view of the Earth sees it as essentially wild and self-organized by means of its own inner power.

Seven centuries ago, St. Francis of Assisi introduced into Christian thinking the idea that wild creatures are part of the spiritual whole of the world. St. Francis' perspective never caught on well in a control-minded Western culture, but it has been waiting in the wings of Christianity since then. St. Francis was designated patron saint of ecologists, thanks in part to Lynn White's 1967 article. There must be a wry smile on the saint's face now to hear from Assisi Hindus and Buddhists speaking for him in the debate over whether nature is ours, or we its.

Living
in a
Greenhouse

M any thinking people have become connoisseurs of catastrophe simply because there are so many dramatic disasters to be anticipated and chosen among. Nuclear threats top most people's lists because of their global and long-term effects. Air and water pollution have been popular perils, lately increased in power by many unfolding stories of acid rain and toxic waste disposal. Some prefer to anticipate economic and social collapses as they contemplate deficits and third-world debts. Part of the appeal of these problems is that all of them are clearly caused by human actions, and so should be solvable by working to change the policies of governments and the habits of people. If human error can damage the world, it figures that responsible human action ought to be able to mend earthly health.

There is another large class of catastrophes which fails to attract organized human resistance. No one holds rallies to protest volcanic eruptions or hurricanes, and people who live in earthquake areas usually develop elaborate rationalizations to justify their no-fault awareness. We find ways to live with genuine natural disasters simply because we know them to be beyond human control. There are some grey catastrophes which do not fit neatly into human or non-human causes. One such may be the greenhouse effect caused by the steady buildup of atmospheric carbon dioxide.

Geologic evidence suggests that CO_2 concentrations and their effects upon the Earth's climate have followed a fairly regular cycle for millions of years. For every 100,000 years of Earth history, we can expect 90,000 to be an ice age, followed by a moderate interglacial period of roughly 10,000 years. While sandwiched in the warm space between glacial periods over the past ten millenia, humans have domesticated animals, invented agriculture and civilization, and lately learned to burn fuels and to clear forests, both of which add significantly to CO_2 accumulations. But people didn't invent or cause the glacial cycle that is triggered by CO_2; it seems that our influence is merely speeding the process along slightly.

What is the appropriate way to think about the greenhouse effect? If we regard it as a problem for people to solve, then the actions required are staggering: remineralize all of the Earth's soils, replace all of the Earth's lost forests, cease all burning of fossil fuels—and accomplish all that in the next few years! Some people are hard at work now to create the political and economic circumstances under which such changes might be made. Their efforts are admirable, and are fully in the heroic tradition of struggling against impossible odds to accomplish superhuman feats. This approach continues the noble but tragic pattern which assumes that whatever happens on Earth has human causes and cures. When disaster impends, dedicated people try to prevent it by seeking greater control over events.

It might be interesting, for a change, to regard the greenhouse effect as a normal part of the Earth's cycles. The question then would not be how to prevent it, but how to learn to live with it? Our species has had plenty of experience at living with ice ages, for we have been around on the planet long enough to have survived several of those 100,000-year cycles. But our memories are short, and our ancestors who coped with ice 10,000 years ago neglected to leave us a manual describing the niceties of ice-age living. Since they survived and prospered, we ought to be able to muddle through as well.

There are people who know how to live well in severe climates, and we will need their advice. Those few arctic residents who have not succumbed to imported technologies from the south may be in high demand to teach the knack of keeping culture in the cold. Skilled Eskimos may replace computer programmers as the experts of choice, especially since computers will not function well without the temperate support systems they depend upon.

During temperate times the Earth produces huge surpluses of everything, but when the ice returns it is time to live again with a tight budget. Numbers of plants, animals, people, and liveable acres must all become much smaller. Systems of all kinds will shrink, and the excess goods and foods that have made industrial and technological cultures possible will no longer support the massive structures that have been built upon them. Small will become necessary, but there is no reason why it should not be beautiful as well.

In an icy world, connoisseurs of catastrophe will also have to scale down their worrying to more intimate dimensions. Nations will be unable to afford nuclear energy and warfare, and defunct industries cannot produce toxic wastes or acid rain. Budget deficits will become less important than heat deficits, and a glacial landscape will do more to control population than planned parenthood or the pill. An ice age will have to be a time of community, with small groups living closely together, sharing and husbanding the available goods. The arts of conversation and storytelling can bloom again, along with crafts of durability.

Making the transition from temperate luxury to frigid frugality will not be easy for the Earth or for any of its creatures. Habits acquired over several thousands of years will not be broken quickly, and people will be no more eager than any other living creatures to do without what they regard as the necessities of life. But think of the strength and resilience that we see in the faces of the victims of floods, hurricanes, and fires when they are interviewed on television. As they rebuild their damaged lives according to new rules, so can we all.

When changes come as part of the natural order of things, people and all other creatures find the wherewithal to accommodate them. Those talents have been acquired over many millions of years, and they are far more valuable than the short-lived illusion that humans are masters of the Earth.

There is no reason why learning to live in a global greenhouse cannot proceed simultaneously with strong efforts to prevent or to postpone the effects of CO_2 concentration. Reforestation, re-mineralization, and decreased use of fossil fuels are excellent ideas no matter what the future holds. But it seems arrogant to assume that we are going to teach an old Earth new habits just to suit human convenience.

Weeds
and the
Right Place

There is no biological definition of weeds. They are not part of any botanical phylum, and no scientist can measure weedy characteristics. Weeds are wild plants whose bad luck it is to grow in domesticated places. Nothing in their genes has warned them of how dangerous gardeners can be to their well-being. In the end, the idea of weeds must be understood by moral and esthetic criteria. Perhaps the best definition is that a weed is any plant that grows where you don't want it.

Lillies growing in wheat fields would be treated like weeds, just as buttercups are in bluegrass lawns or pastures. Weeds are simply in the wrong place, not for their own interests, but only because of human tastes. Our species decided at the origin of agriculture that we would choose the right place for certain plants and exclude all others. Weeds are a confused category of plant life lacking identity and without evolutionary history, for they are nothing but a human idea. Endless hours of gardening toil and millions of tons of herbicides are devoted annually to the enforcement of that idea.

In recent research, microbiologists have found it possible to alter organisms genetically so as to cause them to choose the wrong habitat and thus condemn themselves to death. These altered organisms have been deliberately confused, but their errors resemble those made by weeds which choose to settle in fastidious gardens. Mistakes that weeds make by accident, humans can make intentionally. For what we think to be good reasons, such as weed and pest control and energy production, we can transform right places into wrong and deadly ones. No fiddling with genes is necessary for this; a culture that persuades us to forget that we are natural organisms is enough.

People can live in concrete environments amidst their toxic wastes just as cattle can live in feed lots or lions in zoos. All are more or less healthy, they eat and reproduce normally, and they even seem happy from time to time. Yet there is in us, as in all creatures, a deep strain of love for all kinds of life. That part of us needs space, enough unpredictability to be interesting, diversity of living forms, and a sense that we are part of processes that we do not control. Profound parts of us long for a right place that is wild, and in our hearts we need weeds.

Who's
Not
An Island

I t was John Donne who said in the seventeenth century that no one is an island. That was a useful way to remind us that we are all connected to the Earth and to one another, and that isolation is an illusion. Without forgetting that, it is also important to remember that there are islands, and that people resemble them in many ways. Each of us is a discrete system of consciousness and organic processes connected to the mainland of life by loosely scheduled ferries and lines of communication.

Even a brief experience of island living teaches one clear lesson: don't depend on the ferries, although you must. Freedom of movement is not an inalienable right, but a gift bestowed by some unpredictable deity in a wheelhouse. Most of the time things work well enough, but there are enough glitches to remind one that island life is not like a well-oiled machine. It resembles instead a child learning to walk.

The ferries kiss the docks and toddle off, leaving the island's seashore boundaries intact. Within those irregular lines life is contained, quiet, and slowly paced. Changes do not happen rapidly, but move as the seasons do, or as organisms grow, mature, and die. Human ways seem to reflect the cyclic nature of the island, and conversations have a way of going nowhere while everyone enjoys the process. There is little point in vigorous purposive action, so no one wastes much time that way until they have to meet the ferry schedule. Being contained makes it easier to relax.

Outside the window is a forest, and beyond that is the sea in all directions, and just beyond the sea are the Cascade and Olympic mountain ranges. The big features of life are all prominent here, each of them a sort of island nurturing particular forms of life and forbidding others. The big threats to life are also evident in the Trident submarine base not many miles away, the notorious nuclear power plants scattered around Washington, and the destructive exploitation of forests, water, and goods that accompanies a culture which is busily undermining itself. This island is no hideaway, but a speck of land that feels what is happening on Earth, creatively and otherwise. While islands exist, hideaways don't.

Where
is
Wilderness?

There are professionals whose work it is to define and measure the characteristics of wilderness. They notice such things as the numbers of plant and animal species per hectare, the histories of roads, trails, and human activities in a given area, and the pressures for development brought by lobbyists who believe that land's "highest and best use" should be profitable. Without these planners who quantify the qualities of wilderness, parks and wilderness areas could not endure in this society.

Those who love wild lands understand that games like this must be played in order to preserve wilderness sites, but they know better in their hearts. Among themselves, they forget the language of measurement and speak of the feelings that accompany a large flock of geese ascending from a remote lake, or the surprise of discovering a fox's track superimposed on their own footprint made an hour ago. The awareness of wilderness is far more profound than its measurement, but only those who cherish that awareness can share it knowingly.

It seems a pity that we have associated wilderness only with landscapes or particular places. We work hard to preserve locales which evoke in us powerful feelings of connectedness with the Earth and its processes, sometimes forgetting that the feelings are what we most want to preserve. True, it is difficult now to have a wilderness experience without a wilderness setting, yet it is worth remembering that they are not exactly the same thing.

We respond to wilderness because it has its counterpart within us. Our species emerged from the wild natural history of the Earth. During all but the most recent moments of time, wilderness was our constant context. We learned to stand and walk within it, borrowed its sounds to make music and language, and nourished the development of our minds in order to explore and understand it. Somewhere along the line, we mistakenly judged that wilderness was "out there," while our kind of creature lived in other places and by different rules. That was when we lost sight of the wild Earth, and of important parts of ourselves.

It is worthwhile to remind ourselves from time to time that wilderness is not only a place, but is also a state of being. It is a state characterized by freedom, self-organization, extravagant variety, complex order, grandness of scale, continual change, orientation in time, and beauty. Those are among the powers that wilderness has over us, but they are also among our powers. We can find and create them in many ways, whatever place we happen to be in. Our best task then, is not only to preserve wilderness settings, but also to try to resemble them more within ourselves, and in what we do.

Minding Four: Obeying

To hear is to obey, for both verbs share the same ancient root. The admonition, "mind your mother," is best understood as the need to listen carefully to the source of our life in order to understand its rules. Mindless obedience will not do, for the rules change subtly and continuously, requiring fresh listening every day. The voice of the Earth speaks through many creatures and places, and the ear must be cocked to catch its modulations. Minding is hearing in order to obey.

Rogation Days

Time was when Christian folk used to celebrate Rogation Days. Rogation is the act of begging or supplicating. It was dignified, even sacred, to beg in those pre-reformation days before possessions and wealth became the surest signs of blessedness. Rogation Days were the three days preceding Ascension Day, and their purpose was to accomplish as much forgiveness and humility as possible before the final ceremony of Easter renewal. It was all right to be a rogue then.

Rogation is a word that has slipped from common usage, but its derivatives are everywhere: abrogate, arrogant, derogatory, interrogate, and surrogate are just a few of the more familiar ones. All of them suggest in one way or another the suspension of lawful normalcy. Abrogation is an invalidation of law; arrogance is haughty pretentiousness; derogatory statements disparage others; interrogation means to question or doubt; a surrogate is a substitute for the real thing. Rogation suggests a way of acting that bends the usual laws a little.

The time seems ripe for renewing the art of rogation. Affluent people could profit from learning how to beg, and from seeking forgiveness. Stuffy people would be happier if they could break their boring habits. Public leaders could gain in humanity if they could occasionally be free of the pompous posing to which they are addicted. All of us would feel better with a little more looseness in our lives. A rogue is at least a living creature, demonstrating its liveliness by stepping beyond the rules of nicety and normalcy now and then. Each of us has a rogue inside reminding us that we have some wildness within.

The rogue I have known best is Oregon's Rogue River. Flowing down the slopes of the Cascade Mountains, it is a wild river. It becomes tamer as it approaches the agricultural valleys, persuaded by dams and diversions to do human bidding, more or less. Then it re-enters the mountains and becomes wild again until it loses itself in the ultimate wilderness, the ocean. Why can't we all live that way, retaining our roguish character, nourishing everything around us, yet responding to the demands made upon us when we have to?

High in the Himalayas, even the Ganges begins as a rogue. The Earth's most used, abused, and sacred rivers — the Volga, the Yukon, the Amazon, the Rhine, the Mississippi, the Danube, the Nile, the Yellow — all arise in the wilderness, and all finally return to it. All are rogues at heart, submitting unwillingly to the manipulations and wastes imposed upon them by human affairs. Now and again all of them break human law with floods and surges of energy that mock and mangle all management devices, reminding people who insist upon living near rivers that they are in a wild neighborhood.

It would be a mistake to pass a law establishing a Rogation Day holiday. Laws are the last things rogues need. A better approach would be for each of us to wake up occasionally, smile roguishly into the mirror, and declare secretly, "this will be a wild day." We would then have a private license to beg a bit, to play tricks, and to sidestep the rules of our lives in novel ways. Like rivers, we could be capricious without being malicious, ignoring temporarily our domesticated selves.

Heraclitus said that you can't step twice into the same river, for rivers constantly rearrange themselves into something new at each instant. The rivers of the Earth have been chosen by humans as the best symbols of change, continuous process, and the flow of time. Rivers make change obvious, but people and all living creatures are in perpetual motion and change as much as rivers are. For the same reasons that you cannot step into the same river twice, no river can wet you twice, providing you practice the art of rogation.

Summer Time

However accurate watches and clocks may be, they fail to tell
the truth about time. My conventional watch (called these
days an "analog" model) is a symbolic arrangement of numbers repre-
senting twelve adjacent hours, with continuously moving hands to
indicate time passing. When I look at it I see a twelve hour span,
and I learn which part of it I am moving through. My watch leaves
it to me to figure out which half of the day it is telling me about,
and usually I can manage to do that. The watch measures time by
rearranging its objects in space, which is analogous to what the solar
system does. The speed of the hour hand is based upon the speed
of the Earth's daily rotation, so when I glance at my wrist I am
reminded that the Earth is in motion.

Digital clocks and watches convey no such sense of context.
Impaired creatures that they are, they are unable to comprehend more
than one instant at a time. They display only points in time, with
nothing to hint that there is a process going on that includes what
went before and what comes after. A digital timepiece resembles a
highly trained specialist who has learned to do only one thing, to
do it very well, and to ignore all surroundings and relationships. Digital

watches and narrow visions fit together very well, and both are signs of our time.

The history of timekeeping looks like a gradual but continuous loss of contact with the sources of time. The builders of megaliths like Stonehenge were participants in cosmic time, and they had to work very hard to keep track of where they were in relation to cosmic goings-on. Sun dials were invented to make things easier, but they limited their users to awareness of solar time on cloudless days. Mechanical clocks left the sun out of the picture, and tried merely to represent the rotation of the Earth. Electronic digital watches have forgotten even the Earth, for they convey the impression that time is an instantaneous numerical event captured on a midget television screen. The information provided by Stonehenge was a complex mixture of practical and spiritual news about the universe, but a digital watch can only tell you whether you are late for lunch.

Whatever tales our time machines may tell about it, time is a process of continuous change. Many of the world's peoples still learn about time by looking at the sky. They see the daily procession of the sun, and they are also aware of the Moon's monthly phases, of the everchanging positions of the planets, and of the continuing adjustments as constellations of stars parade the night sky. Plants and animals also proclaim the many stages of the seasons, and an experienced observer of them knows for sure when it is safe to begin a garden or to expect certain migratory birds and fish to appear. Sadly, strapping watches to our wrists seems to obscure all of these connections, leaving us with nothing but a few numbers to represent the flowing stream of time.

In the interest of accuracy, minds need to be reset from time to time by consulting the sky and the surrounding natural world. A summer vacation can be a good opportunity for stepping out of mechanical or electronic time measurement and into the Earth's real time. Clocks and watches will scarcely fret if they lose their audiences for a while, and most of them will keep on ticking from their tiny batteries if they are left at home in a drawer. Their owners, however, may make discoveries when they begin to learn how high the sun stands at breakfast, and how vivid are the stars at bedtime.

The time of summer is special, and it deserves to be delivered from binding schedules and small visions. Its themes of freedom, sunlight, and growth need to be celebrated. A holiday from the machines of time is a good way to enjoy the rediscovery that time is not a succession of bits and pieces, but a seamless pattern of natural change.

The
Trillium
Strategy

I t is always a treat to find a trillium in the spring, but this year they
overwhelmed me. Arriving earlier in the year than I usually do
at an old mountain haunt, I found myself in a profusion of these small
triple-petalled flowers set off against their three distinctive green leaves
on a single slim stalk. They were in and near a much-used trail,
growing around picnic tables in a campground, and abundant near
a river swimming hole where families with kids play all summer long.
I had never seen them so luxuriant, although I have come here every
spring for more than thirty years.

Often I have rounded a bend in that trail in midsummer to find
vacationing gardeners furtively digging up small vine maples,
dogwoods, or even streamside joint grass to transplant to their home
gardens. They seem not to know or care that this is a protected
wilderness area. How had those petty thieves missed the trillium, and
why had I failed to know of their abundance during my years of
walking that trail? I had always treasured finding one as a rare
discovery, and kept its whereabouts to myself for fear that someone
might nab it. But clearly, the trillium did not need my help to
survive, for they were managing to reproduce in spite of heavy traffic
and grabby gardeners. They have a strategy.

Trillium are members of the lily family, growing from rhizomes where their energy is stored. The species I was looking at, *Trillium ovatum*, sends up its single stalk promptly when the winter snow melts, and is the first flower to bloom in the spring. Flowers are usually white at first, then pass through stages of pink and dusty rose as they age. Within three weeks the flower is generally gone, and the leaves tend to disappear among the other small plants of the forest floor. Seeds mature in late summer, and are often transported by ants who are attracted to the oily substance that glues the seeds together. Once its flowering is over, the summer work of storing energy and producing seeds proceeds subtly, unnoticed by most people.

It is dangerous to be as beautiful and delicate as the flowering trillium is. The plant conveys joy to most people who see it. If any plant can be said to dance, trillium can. Its delicate, understated design is one that most gardeners would proudly display. Such beauty is seldom left to itself, for someone always seems bent upon possessing it or improving upon it. Any handsome plant or attractive woman will probably encounter many presumptive managers dedicated to making their beauty as useful and profitable as possible.

Yet the trillium is not often cultivated because it is so "difficult." Transplants often fail, and seeds are hard to find and may require three years to germinate. Picked flowers wilt quickly, and only the naive or the foolish would gather them. The plant will not replace a lost bloom. One flower, once a year at just the right time, is all the trillium is prepared to provide. The trillium's habits make it commercially impractical, and too much trouble for all but the most avid enthusiasts. So it remains quietly but emphatically a wild plant, unsuited to exploitation.

Trillium developed their strategy long before there were people around to pick them. Blooming before the tourists arrive, then blending in with other plants, permits them to survive undetected in dangerous environments. And their way of life prevents them from having to endure the manipulations that are imposed upon more tractable plants like tulips and roses. The trillium are simply lucky to be following an inherited path that happens to be effective for retaining their integrity. It is their good fortune to be useless.

The Taoist philosopher Chuang Tzu told in the fourth century, B.C., of the value of uselessness. His example was a gnarled old oak tree that had been allowed to live its full life span because its grain was too crooked to make furniture and too difficult to split for firewood. The tree appeared in a dream to a carpenter, and compared itself with fruit trees and straight-grained timber: "Their utility makes life miserable for them. ...as for me, I've been trying for a long time to be of no use, and this is of great use to me." The oak's strategy for survival was to be as ugly and deformed as possible, thus gaining a full life for itself by being useless to others.

The message of the trillium is that one needn't be ugly to be useless, and that it is possible to be beautiful while still retaining the benefits of uselessness. This summer I will remember that there are trillium hiding just out of vision within inches of the footsteps of acquisitive travelers who pass them by. They will never be domesticated because their lives are too complex to be manageable by others. Their uselessness assures that they will remain free and wild. The trillium will take the summer to collect their energy, and they will be ready to bloom again in their own time next spring, probably when no one is watching.

Is
the Earth
Alive?

Most people have ready answers to the question: obviously yes, or obviously no. The strong positions behind either answer are supported by personal intuitions, mystic traditions, empirical science, or even engineering and business considerations. Unresolvable as these different perspectives are, their adherents usually agree in the end that the answer to the question must depend upon how "alive" is to be defined.

The origins of the verb "to live" are unexpected, but provocative. Both the Sanscrit root *(limpati)* and the Indo-European root *(lip)* mean "smeared" or "sticky." The basic idea, say the scholars, is " 'to be sticky, hence 'to adhere,' hence 'to remain or stay,' especially 'to stay alive,' hence simply 'to live' " (Partridge, Walshe, Webster). Smeared and sticky as it is, the idea of life seems to have grown in human consciousness as an awareness of moist persistence. If our ancient ancestors could visit us today, they might point to wet Velcro as a symbol of what it means to be alive.

If living things are those which persist and remain, then the Earth is much more alive than any of the plant or animal species which inhabit its surfaces. Its years are counted in the multi-billions, while we organisms who also live here have only had a few millions of years to develop our various forms and lifestyles. The new awareness of cosmic time has changed the way we think about the meaning of life. That is one reason why it is necessary to ask anew, is the Earth a living organism? The question has to do with time.

Knowledge of history is important, but it is now necessary to be aware also of the larger scope of pre-historic time. History, as taught by most educational systems, consists of the acts and accomplishments of nations, influential people, and technological developments. Beyond that stretches the far greater expanse of evolutionary, cosmic, and mythic time. Time, not history, is the place to look for the origins and meaning of life.

The story of life is a cosmic tale. The Earth that we know is a lively, and probably living, part of one galactic system among many in a universe of unimaginable age and complexity. Whether familiar forms of biological life exist elsewhere or not, still our small example on this planet is enough to show that organic life is a chapter in the cosmic story. Human life is a short but pithy paragraph in that story, and the history of civilizations is but a dependent clause in the sentence most recently spoken. Only the whole system can tell the whole story.

The definition of life has many components. Simplemindedly, humans have often taken themselves to be the main source of criteria for classifying all life. We hear talk of "lower" forms of life which can reproduce themselves but lack sentience, and others which have sentience but lack languages, and of the very highest forms which sport not only language, but also have sufficient consciousness to invent theologies and Velcro. Now it is possible to transcend such narrow views and begin to construct a vision of whole systems of life which have evolved through self-organization.

In the emerging view that many scientists are pioneering, life is seen as a process of self-regulation where a rich interplay of novelty and stability interact to produce new creations. This has been called *The Gaia Hypothesis*, in honor of the Earth mother in Greek mythology.

The most sophisticated modern science is now begining to affirm ancient wisdom, both agreeing that the Earth and all the systems upon it and around it are active parts of a living cosmic whole. If the cosmos is alive, how could the Earth be otherwise?

It has seemed otherwise for only a brief and aberrant period. It was in the seventeenth century that a blossoming young science persuaded people that the Earth was inert matter and raw materials. The Earth since then has seemed more like a machine than like an organism, and it has been treated accordingly. Fortunately, that strange episode in history is coming to an end. Our ancient ancestors were right: life *is* sticky and persistent, and it is smeared all over the universe.

Hearty
Conversation

Words and language have generally been thought of as things that humans possess and use, like tools or armies or credit cards, in the service of their goals and purposes. But what if language, rather than being a possession, is more like a process that we participate in? That point was made in the early 1960's by Michael Oakeshott, who argued that language is not primarily a means for acquiring and storing knowledge, nor for manipulating the world, nor even for understanding ourselves, but it is a means through which we take our part in what he called "the Conversation of Mankind." The creature that converses, endlessly, is the human being.

Considered so, conversation is not merely a means to an end such as agreement, conquest, prosperity, or the acquisition of truth, but is an end in itself. Other animals remind us by their examples that all of life's practical necessities for food, shelter, reproduction, and survival can be made without chatting much about them. Like them, we can thrive on Earth without conversation. Perhaps the most basic use of conversation is to orient us in time and space, and to provide continuing checks upon our relationships with the other processes going on around us. Maybe conversation is an elaborate way of calling, as birds do, "I'm here; Where are you?" and listening for a like response in reply.

Conversation is a conventional activity, and its rules change often in response to new circumstances. Richard Rorty, in *Philosophy and the Mirror of Nature* (Princeton University Press, 1979) extended Thomas Kuhn's notion of "paradigms" in science to apply to other human patterns of knowledge, and noted that there is always a standard of "normal discourse" shared by communities of thinking people. Normal discourse is conversation that proceeds according to accepted assumptions about what is true and false, what is relevant and irrelevant, what is an interesting or a stupid question, and what are proper and improper ways for proceeding. People who receive good grades, promotions, or research grants, are usually proficient at normal discourse. Society provides schooling to assure that people will learn how to discourse normally.

Rorty also speaks about "abnormal discourse," or conversation that breaks or ignores accepted conventions. People who converse abnormally may seem nutty to others, but sometimes they introduce ways of talking that change the rules for everyone. The only way to tell whether bizarre artists, revolutionaries, or other oddballs are going to be significant or not is to wait and see whether they can inspire others to converse in their new languages. Socrates got in trouble for his abnormal discourse, but he changed the language of inquiry for all who followed him.

There may be at least two kinds of abnormal discourse. One kind is simply odd speech that breaks contemporary conventions, whatever they may be at a given time. A more profound abnormality, however, occurs when people depart from the patterns of conversation that have been established during the evolutionary history of our species. Such abnormal discourse can seem to be normal when it is affirmed by the conventions of surrounding culture, but it still does violence to the biological history that we also carry within us. Our bodies, not our peers, speak out against abnormal discourse that ignores biological reality.

Perhaps the mechanistic philosophy of modern Western culture has taught people to ignore the messages of the human heart. Descartes, Freud, and the powerful voices of industrial civilization have educated people to an abnormal kind of discourse that ignores the messages of the body and distorts our conversations with one another. The recognition of feelings that are rooted in biological states has been lost, and with it went our capacity for healthy communication that gives expression to feelings. The typical maladies of industrial civilization, hypertension and cardiovascular disease, are in part products of a culture that has distorted the rules of human discourse.

One approach to heart trouble is that of Laurens van der Post, whose book *The Heart of the Hunter* (New York, William Morrow, 1961) opened to the world the complex mental and spiritual lives of African hunting peoples. Among the Kalahari Bushmen, van der Post found the habit of pausing to listen to a "knocking" or a "tapping" within themselves. The knocking is a sign that something unseen needs to be attended to. It is a signal from within one's own body, often quite specifically located in a particular bodily organ. When it happens, Bushmen stop what they are doing and listen carefully to the messages from within themselves. The news may be that someone is about to arrive from a distance, or that there is something wrong with the way one is acting, or that the weather is changing, or danger is present, or any of a host of things that may be happening in unseen ways. It is an internalized communication system that mediates the continuing conversation carried on between the bodies of the Bushmen and the entire human and natural world around them. That conversation is essential to their well-being. As the Bushmen told van der Post, "only a fool will not listen to the knocking that goes on inside himself." For van der Post the knocking represents "the universal language of man." It is a language of the heart.

The conversation of mankind is an open and continuing dialogue that connects our bodies and minds intimately with the processes of nature that permeate all life forms. Whether we call it blood pressure or knocking does not matter. What matters is that we learn to attend, to respond, to express its meaning, and to participate more fully in the conversation of life.

Conversation is not just a matter of people talking with people, and the languages of human speech are not the only languages that matter. The living Earth is a complex of communication with exacting standards for appropriate discourse among its many participants. Tolerance for abnormal expression is high, but not without limits. Sloppy or corrupt language may be merely disorienting, or it may be lethal. Learning to converse well with the world can begin by listening carefully to the messages sent ceaselessly by our bodies and by the other forms of life that share this planet. The best conversations are still those that play variations on the great and ancient theme, "I'm here; Where are you?"

Midwinter
Energy

Holiday seasons require plenty of energy. Winter is one thing, with the greater need it creates for artificial warmth reflected in higher heating bills and heavier clothing. But holidays demand other kinds of energy as well. Money and emotion mingle in Christmas giving, and in the parties, festivities and stresses of celebrating. Small wonder that people feel used up by January, and some even lean toward suicide or psychosis. Holiday seasons are anything but energy efficient. Maybe Christmas is a good time to think about being exhausted, because that is what most of us feel like.

Midwinter rituals began long before Christmas did. People have felt the need to renew themselves in the midst of cold and darkness for hundreds of thousands of seasonal cycles. Somewhere along the line things became confused, and the midwinter yearning for the return of solar energy turned into a massive expenditure that sapped our strength rather than restoring it. Christmas became a Squanderfest, and lost much of its potential power for joy, hope and for giving courage to endure until the sun returned.

Christmas candles are tiny suns that we light in midwinter darkness. The wax and wick store solar energy which is released as light and heat when they burn. Once released, there is no way to reverse the process and recreate a candle from the lost light and heat. Radiation is the end of energy's participation in the living process, and it is irreversible.

The Earth is a candle, too. Like our flashy Christmases, we have learned to make the Earth burn more brightly by dreaming up new ways to ignite some of its elements such as petroleum and radio-active minerals. Cheery though such fires may seem, they are in danger of burn-out, as we are, because of too much intensity. Anything that hot is also sure to be dangerous. Burning the world's wick at a fast pace makes for brief brilliance, perhaps to be followed by profound darkness.

Midwinter is a good time to husband energy of all kinds, physical and emotional. Like the sun, we might do well to shine less at this time of year, not more. The best warmth comes from closeness with one another and with our environment, and the best light is that of understanding. No quantity of therms, candlepower or money has ever created a joyful holiday in the absence of those inner energies.

The point of midwinter rituals is to remind us that life proceeds according to solar cycles. Our tilted, orbiting planet can be depended upon to regain a warmer aspect again if we are just patient with it. There is no need to burn our houses down in order to keep warm, and no need to use up the Earth's substances as if there were no tomorrow. Instead, it would be wise to bend better efforts toward learning to use the sun more and the Earth less in our search for the energy needed for life.

E.F. Schumacher reminded us that small is beautiful: small technology, small consumption, small babies in mangers, small festivities, small hangovers. We may need a small, beautiful Christmas and solar energy in the New Year.

Living
like a
Glacier

R ecently I met a glacier whose lifestyle I admire. Kennicott
is its name, and its address is the Wrangell Mountains of
Alaska. It is in the earth-moving business, crushing and transporting
millions of tons of rock from high places to lower places. Glaciers
have a reputation for being slow-moving, almost lazy, but that
idea must have come from people who observed them from great
distances. Living near the Kennicott, listening to its ceaseless
gnashing and crashing, and watching the rocks that fall from
its faces and the churning chocolate-colored rivers that flow from
it, this glacier felt like a frenzy of purposeful activity. Considering
its huge bulk and its heavy responsibilities, the Kennicott Glacier is
a speedster.

Well-run glaciers live within strict budgets. Their income is
snowfall, and each year's accumulation determines precisely what
the Kennicott can accomplish during its fiscal year. In periods
of abundant snowfall, the Kennicott expands its length and depth
and moves its ice and rocks downslope much faster. But snowfall
has been lean in recent decades, so the Kennicott has cut back
its activities sharply, and is receding at about 100 feet per year.

This glacier is distressed by a surplus, and it abhors deficits. Any household or government would do well to follow its example.

In the early parts of this century, a mining company borrowed the glacier's name and misspelled it. The Kennecott Company, like the Kennicott Glacier, was in the business of moving rocks down the mountainside, but the company limited its attention to those rocks bearing copper ore. Passionate for profits but mindless of budgets, the company operated side by side with the glacier for only twenty-six years before it collapsed. Decaying buildings, rusted machinery, and a rotted railroad are all that remain of the mining operation. Some few fortunes were made and probably expended elsewhere to move other rocks for human gain. Another legacy of the Kennecott mine today is the severe arsenic poisoning of Puget Sound near Tacoma, where the ore from Alaska was processed. No glacier could have accomplished that.

The Kennicott Glacier is in the midst of the largest and least developed national park in the United States, The Wrangell-St. Elias National Park. Facing one another, the Kennicott Glacier and the ruins of the Kennecott mine stand as symbols of powerful American values. America created the idea of national parks out of a love of wildness and in recognition of the necessity of wilderness for the fulfillment of the human spirit. Americans, more than any other people, also invented the means to exploit wilderness and to convert its gifts into short-term profits. When we think like miners we make messes; if we could think like glaciers we might make Yosemites.

Aldo Leopold reminded us that wisdom involves "thinking like a mountain." One could just as easily think like a glacier, or a tree, or a river, or a bear. Whatever the natural model we choose, our thinking will necessarily be governed by awareness of life as a context and process, and our sense of time will need to expand. Listening to the Kennicott Glacier, I heard messages from long ago and far ahead. Rocks that fell onto the moraine where I stood had been moving with the ice for hundreds or thousands of years. Up above, near the head of the glacier, other rocks were plucked from the mountain at the time of my birth, and they will not be heard from again until I have been gone for a millenium or so. If I can use my little time as well as the glacier uses its big time, my life will be well spent.

Glaciers make impressions upon their mountains, and upon those of us who watch them. They radiate dignity, but their feet are dirty with the soil of hard labor. They are above worrying about tidiness. Their direction and movement are never in doubt, for glaciers always know where they are going. They move with the confidence of accepted inevitability. They feel alive, sharing in the processes that all life knows. Living like a glacier requires power without aggression, thinking big while living frugally, and sensitive adjustments to daily and seasonal change. One could do much worse than to live like a glacier.

Photo by Margaret Walker

Joseph Meeker walks tangible and metaphoric trails. He has lived in and strolled across much of Alaska, California, Oregon, and now Washington. Language and ideas are another wilderness through which he feels his way in search of context and meaning. His home is on Vashon Island near Seattle.

The Latham Foundation for the Promotion of Humane Education, a private operating California foundation, was established by Oakland philanthropists Edith Latham and her brother, Milton Latham, in 1918. The Foundation's purpose is manifested in the founders' belief in the basic goodness of all peoples in that humane attitudes and actions can be developed and realized through understanding derived from education.

The Foundation has used its resources to produce and distribute printed and filmed educational materials and publications. Latham's television program series are viewed by millions in this country and abroad.

The objectives of promoting respect for all life are best summarized by the Foundation's charter: "to inculcate the higher principles of humaneness upon which the unity and happiness of the world depend; to emphasize the spiritual fundamentals that lead to world friendship; to promote character building by an understanding of universal kinship; to foster a deeper understanding of and sympathy with man's relations—the animals—who cannot speak for themselves."

The Latham Foundation
Latham Plaza Building
Clement and Schiller Streets
Alameda, Calif. 94501
(415) 521-0920